Dragon Bytes

Chinese Information-War Theory and Practice from 1995-2003

Timothy L. Thomas

Foreign Military Studies Office
Fort Leavenworth, Kansas
2004

The author works for the Foreign Military Studies Office (FMSO), Fort Leavenworth, Kansas. FMSO is a component of the U.S. Army's Training and Doctrine Command (TRADOC). The office is charged with preparing studies and assessments based on the reading of foreign and domestic publications, and through contacts with a network of foreign and U.S. military and civilian security specialists. FMSO researches, writes, and publishes from unclassified sources about the military establishments, doctrines, and practices of selected foreign armed forces. It also studies a variety of civil-military and transnational security issues affecting the U.S. and its military forces. FMSO products are prepared for the U.S. Army and other services, the Department of Defense, as well as non-DoD organizations to include the Treasury and Justice Departments.

FOREWORD

This work examines China's information-war (IW) theory and practice from 1995-2003. The effort rests upon the author's sustained and diligent research in Chinese open sources. Some specialists among the international audience may be surprised by the themes addressed in these sources and the presentation of key issues. The Chinese openly discuss not only computer network attacks and electronic preemption but also the development of IW units and an "integrated network-electronic warfare" theory (which closely approximates the US theory of "network-centric warfare").

Of special interest is the Chinese development of an IW theory that is representative of their country's philosophy and culture. By creating an "IW theory with Chinese characteristics" the People's Liberation Army (PLA) has offered an alternate way of viewing the application of IW than in the West. For example, the Chinese are integrating IW theory into such concepts as a "network People's War" that encourages the nation to be ready to attack networks in the event of a conflict and to conduct protracted IW operations. Additionally, new methods of applying IW are discussed, such as using electrons to implement strategies; and new areas of emphasis, such as information control alongside information superiority. Chinese analysts have attained a greater appreciation and understanding of the application of IW's power from their review of US and coalition actions in the Gulf War, the conflict over Kosovo, and the 2003 Iraqi War. The PLA has analyzed these impressions and lessons learned during the past several years.

The military reader and security specialist will enjoy this different perspective that discusses several areas where US theorists have not tread to date. The findings will prove to be slightly alarming to those who believe that the Chinese are years behind other nations in information age developments.

Dr. Jacob W. Kipp
Director, Foreign Military Studies Office
June 2004

DEDICATION

This book is dedicated to my parents, Robert and Margaret Thomas, and to the memory of my wife's parents, Arthur and Hilda Aberegg. My wife and I thank them for their support, guidance, and positive influence on our lives, and for encouraging us to be inquisitive and understanding of other cultures.

TABLE OF CONTENTS

ACKNOWLEDGEMENT

The author used only open-source translations for the construction of this document. Since the author does not speak Chinese, he fully utilized the translation talents at the Foreign Broadcast Information Service (FBIS) in order to write this work. The author, of course, is solely responsible for the analysis of the material translated by FBIS.

The work of FBIS through the years has enabled many American analysts to better understand foreign cultures and interpret events. Their help has been invaluable. For their continued support and professional work, the author extends to FBIS translators and managers his deepest gratitude and appreciation. Without their assistance, past generations of US analysts would have fallen far short in the thorough and competent performance of their duties. It is the author's hope that government funding for FBIS increases dramatically in the coming years to support the war on terrorism and other emerging threats confronting the United States.

Further, the author would like to acknowledge the absolutely vital support of four individuals who assisted with this project. First, Mr. Karl Prinslow, director of the Joint Reserve Intelligence Center at Fort Leavenworth, is cited for his enthusiasm to see this project realized and completed. Without Mr. Prinslow's initial push, this project would still be languishing. Second, the author would like to thank the director of the Foreign Military Studies Office, Dr. Jacob Kipp, for his support and encouragement along the way. Dr. Kipp's words of advice, as always, were a cause for further consideration and the addition of topics that escaped the author's attention. Third, the author would like to thank Ms. Cathy Elliott of the Center for Army Lessons Learned (CALL). For the past three years Ms. Elliott has provided outstanding graphic support as exemplified by the cover material for this publication. Finally, the author would like to thank Christine Thomas, his wife, for her patience and thought provoking questions as she read through the manuscript. She spent hours reading and correcting the work as necessary. Her professionalism and attention to detail have made this a much better work.

INTRODUCTION

This work views the Chinese military as an emerging competitor in the field of information war (IW). In the business world, it is important to know who the competition is and what his or her methods are. This thinking applies to the military as well. A close study of how China is constructing its information war theory and practice is of crucial value to Western analysts. In similar fashion Chinese analysts are closely perusing US IW articles and journals.

While many people know that the information age has dawned in China, they do not realize how fast it is developing in the military sector. For example, in 2003 virtual reality became a standard operating procedure for training exercises as well as for command and staff exercises. The first group of graduates of a class specializing in armored-reconnaissance command operations participated in drills that used unmanned aerial vehicles (UAVs), radar, and computers to collect and process intelligence information. Additionally, the military reportedly developed a "fingerprint plus password" e-mail system among many other information technology (IT) developments. Finally, of more immediate concern to the US, one important Chinese writer suggested that China be prepared to conduct preemption operations in the form of computer network attacks in order to gain the initiative in future war.

These developments are not taking place under a dense shroud of secrecy, and this is fortunate for the West. China's transparency may indicate that they are not as threatening as some expect. During the past ten years, hundreds of Chinese military and civilian scholars published articles and books on information war and related issues (networking, information theory, simulations, information security, etc.) that were significant for their thoroughness and creativity. These writings were in response to extensive IW developments worldwide but in particular to those in the West. Further, these developments responded to China's internal requirement to modernize and train its own force in the application of new information technologies. On numerous occasions in 2003, China's leaders stressed the requirement for the People's Liberation Army (PLA) to move from a mechanized to an "informationized" force (as the Chinese refer to it). Without such advances, they warned, China's armed forces would fall far behind the military capabilities of smaller nations.

An analysis of the works of China's outstanding corps of IW specialists demonstrates that their IW theory is imbedded with "Chinese characteristics." This means that IW theory has taken account of Chinese military culture and philosophy. An example is the extensive integration of stratagems into IW theory. Stratagems are clever schemes and methods to seize and maintain information supremacy or control in order to help a force prevail in IW. This factor is often not adequately addressed in US writings.

Additionally, China is quickly integrating IW theory into its People's War concept. People's War was previously understood to mean that China, in the event of an invasion, would rise up quickly and conduct guerilla warfare against an invader. The theory is now updated. People's War can include a multitude of computer operators who use laptops to conduct "take home battle" against an electronic invader of China's borders. This development is not fully understood or appreciated in the West, but it is one with significant strategic and operational implications.

Chinese military science dictates that IW is divided into sub-elements very different from those studied in the United States. These sub-elements include the forms, nature, features, distinctions, principles, types, circles, and levels of IW. These sub-elements are similar to Russia's military science methodology. Both Russia and China derive their military theory from Marxist-Leninist thought and utilize the dialectic thought process when evaluating the operational environment.

Chinese theorists are developing, then, an IW theory that reflects their culture and practice. There is a reason for this. Major General Dai Qingmin, head of the Fourth Department of the Chinese General Staff, stated that:

> Under the premise of following the objective rules for the construction of informationization, only with superior thought processes and superior moves, and by seeking a developmental strategy of "imbalance" will we truly be able to avoid traveling the "path that the enemy expects." In the realm of IW, trying to keep up with the Jones' by developing whatever they possess will lead to falling into the traps set by others; regardless of how rapidly we develop, it will still be hard to escape being controlled by other people.[1]

While pursuit of an IW theory has proven fruitful, turning theory into practice has been more difficult. China is still developing the civilian and military infrastructure to support their philosophy.[2] While not quite an IW force with which to reckon yet on the battlefield, the Chinese are making tremendous strides nonetheless. The PLA has conducted numerous, large-scale IW exercises over the past few years. They now reportedly train IW brigades in offensive and defensive tactics. Various branches of the armed forces have also constructed several high-tech laboratories to simulate IW effects and outcomes. Further, the PLA has studied the potential development of an independent "net force" branch of service to supplement the navy, army and air force. Thus, to a significant degree the PLA has successfully inculcated Chinese characteristics into its IW theory and is working hard at turning theory into practice.

---

[1] Dai Qingmin, "On the Development of Army Informationization and Information Warfare," Zhongguo Junshi Kexue (China Military Science), 20 December 2002, pp. 66-70 as translated and downloaded from the FBIS Web site on 20 December 2003.
[2] The cornerstone of IW's operational theory, to some Chinese theorists, involves preserving the integrity and stability of the infrastructure of one's side to perform these functions. Infrastructure stability is more important than survivability of units. See Wang Jianghuai and Lin Dong, "Viewing Our Army's Quality Building from the Perspective of What Information Warfare Demands," Jiefangjun Bao (Liberation Army Daily), 3 March 1998, p. 6 as translated and downloaded from the FBIS Web site on 16 March 1998.

This book will highlight key aspects of the Chinese approach to IW.[3] Unlike the US Armed Forces, which publishes its IW theory in joint publications and field manuals as doctrine for its forces,[4] the PLA does not produce a single, definitive work representing a concise and coherent view of Chinese military thinking on IW. This book represents the end result of an extensive analysis of open-source Chinese documents on IW. It attempts to draw a historical picture of the development of Chinese IW theory over the past ten years and to explain how it differs from US theory. This volume does not presume that Chinese IW is the new "threat" to the West. Rather, the purpose is to uncover new areas of focus and interest for American analysts. And in this regard, China's writings on IW offer much food for thought.

The first chapter examines Chinese IW theory and practice from 1995 to 2000. It discusses how the information age has affected China's attitude toward warfare and specific Chinese historical factors affecting this interpretation. This chapter also explores the development of Chinese IW definitions, training courses, and organizational structures that emerged during this period.

The second chapter takes a look at selected works of Shen Weiguang, one of China's premier IW warriors. Dr. Shen discusses such concepts as the theory of information deterrence and offers suggestions for the development of IW rules of engagement and strategies for deterring IW, concepts rarely addressed by US IW specialists. Further, Shen emphasizes the Chinese concept of "control" as a focus of its IW theory.

Chapter Three presents the continuation of IW thinking in China from 2001 through December 2003. The material is thought provoking as Chinese experts discuss offensive IW units and the concepts of preemption and wars of annihilation via computer nets. Theoreticians also point out Chinese interest in information supremacy and in a concept known as "integrated network-electronic warfare" which approximates the US concept of network-centric warfare.

Chapter Four discusses China's IW stratagems and how they fit into the Chinese understanding of IW. The Chinese are using technology to implement ancient stratagems in ways unfamiliar to Western audiences, and they are aiming much of their effort at influencing human decision making. Like Chapter Three, this chapter offers much for Western analysts to consider.

Chapter Five presents an overview of Chinese psychological operations (PSYOP). China's PSYOP specialists think that intimidation and power are twin concepts and that perception warfare will play a key role in future diplomatic and military confrontation. This emphasis on PSYOP is reminiscent of Sun Tzu's desire to "win without fighting."

---

[3] There may be inconsistencies in some translations of specific words or concepts in this work of which the author is unaware. Since the author does not speak Chinese, he could not independently check translations conducted by numerous translators.

[4] To find the US publication on information operations, conduct a simple Google search for JP 3-13. The search turns up the Web site and PDF document at http://www.dtic.mil/doctrine/jel/new_pubs/jp3_13.pdf

Chapter Six discusses Chinese perceptions of the coalition battle for Iraq in March and April of 2003. Chapter Seven highlights Chinese perceptions of the battle for Iraq from May to August 2003. Chapter Eight is a list of conclusions drawn from the chapters in this book.

Appendix One highlights the fifty or so articles in the journal of the Chinese Academy of Military Science, China Military Science, that discuss information warfare and related issues. Appendix Two is a Taiwanese article about Chinese IW. It provides the reader with a comparative look at how the Taiwanese view Chinese IW. (No analysis of Appendix Two is provided.)

With this background in mind, it is time to begin a journey into the world of Chinese IW.[5]

---

[5] No specific pages will be listed for quotes from all the articles used in the preparation of this article. The reason is that printouts of FBIS translations do not correlate to the pages in the original Chinese document.

CHAPTER ONE: CHINESE INFORMATION-WAR THEORY AND PRACTICE: 1995-2000

IW with Chinese Characteristics

By the end of the period 1995–2000, US officials had become aware of the growing influence of IW on Chinese military thought. For example, the FY2000 report on China presented to Congress by the Secretary of Defense (as mandated by the National Defense Authorization Act) indicated growth in Chinese IW theory and capability.[6] The report noted that since the 7 May 1999 bombing of the Chinese embassy in Belgrade by NATO air forces, the Chinese leadership accelerated military modernization, pursued strategic cooperation with Russia, and increased its proliferation activities. In particular, China focused efforts on potential adversaries that possessed advanced information technologies and long-range, precision weapons. They also focused on updating their own "active defense" doctrine that concentrated on conducting what is sometimes called "People's War under modern conditions."

China's military was somewhat surprised when IW theory first appeared in US articles in the early 1990s and later when it was inserted into its field exercises. Even though Chinese analysts had written about IW theory since about 1985, it had done little to advance or apply the concept. Rather, IW appeared to be a subject for future generations to handle since the Chinese were depending upon a mechanized force sufficient for the present.

The first Gulf War changed this attitude. Chinese military analysts viewed with awe the power and precision of an information-based force for the first time on a modern battlefield—a force far removed from Chinese standards. China's leaders realized that without incorporating information technology into their weaponry and equipment that the PLA risked being left behind in the dustbin of military history.

At first Chinese thinking reflected, and perhaps even followed, US developments in the mainstream press. Chinese IW definitions sounded much like US definitions. This may have been done on purpose so that everyone could speak the same language or perhaps because there was no developed IW theory with Chinese characteristics. Behind the scenes, however, a debate was unfolding that put IW at the forefront of future military plans. The decision to develop IW theory with Chinese characteristics apparently crystallized around the 1997-1998 time frame.

The military journal China Military Science, produced by China's Academy of Military Science, began to publish a steady stream of IW related articles in the late 1990s which continues to this day. (See Appendix One for a list of these articles.) In one of these articles, which compared the psychological-war (PSYWAR) capabilities (an IW component) of the West and China, it was noted:

---

[6] The Report to Congress Pursuant to the FY2000 National Defense Authorization Act, downloaded from http://www.defenselink.mil/news/Jun2000/china06222000.htm

Differences in environment, cultural traditions, political systems, economic strength, national defense capability and national spiritual belief lead to a great distinction in various nations in subjective cognition, ideological basis, principles of application and structures of organization of PSYWAR.[7]

By underscoring several differences between US and Chinese thinking, the article also reflected areas where China's approach to IW would differ from that in the West. A quality IW force allows China, as it does other nations, to theoretically become a threat to more powerful nations. IW empowered nations can potentially conduct electronic attacks against a nation's financial institutions and impact the worldwide economy since millions of financial transactions are carried out on the Internet.

Not surprisingly, based on this and other evidence, Chinese theorists and leaders have called for a move from a mechanized PLA force to an informationized force. It makes complete sense to put a significant effort into developing an information-based capability in both the civilian and military arenas if it helps a force catch up with an opponent. From the Chinese point of view, IW makes their forces more combat worthy than ever before. China's leaders also feel the information age offers a window of opportunity for China's military to catch up, and perhaps even surpass the US and other nations, with an informationized force and to leap beyond mechanized-age weaponry. From a Chinese point of view, such advances are like "adding wings to a tiger."

Reports of hacker attacks on US labs indicate that China is moving from theory to practice. The Washington Times reported on 3 August 2000 that hackers suspected of working for a Chinese government institute broke into a Los Alamos computer system and took large amounts of sensitive, but unclassified, information. Los Alamos spokesman Jim Danneskiold stated that "an enormous amount of Chinese activity hitting our green, open sites" occurs continuously.[8]

Targets of Chinese IW include information sources, channels, destinations,[9] and C4I (command, control, communications, computers and intelligence), and electronic-warfare assets. Some note that the initial targets of a Chinese IW attack will be the computer networking systems linking political, economic, and military installations of a country (as well as society in general) and the capability to conduct decision making and coordinated actions. This implies that both cognitive and information systems are hit.[10] Some Chinese theorists have recommended organizing network special warfare

[7] Wang Lingshui, Ma Jingcheng, and Yan Jianhong, "Comparison of PSYWAR between China and the West," China Military Science, Number 6, 2000, pp. 102-110 as translated and downloaded from the FBIS Web site on 10 April 2001.
[8] Bill Gertz, "Hackers Linked to China Stole Documents from Los Alamos," The Washington Times, 3 August 2000, p. 1.
[9] Wang Jianghuai and Lin Dong, "Viewing Our Army's Quality Building from the Perspective of What Information Warfare Demands," Beijing Jiefangjun Bao, 3 March 1998, p. 6 as translated and downloaded from the FBIS Web site on 16 March 1998.
[10] Shen Weiguang, "Checking Information Warfare-Epoch Mission of Intellectual Military," Jiefangjun Bao, 2 February 1999, p. 6 as translated and downloaded from the FBIS Web site on 17 February 1999.

detachments and computer experts to form a shock brigade of "network warriors" to accomplish this task. These detachments will look for critical nodes and control centers on networks and sabotage them.[11]

Chinese theorists believe that the capabilities and qualities of the information era enhance and breathe new life into Mao Zedong's theory of a People's War. Chinese IW specialist General Wang Pufeng noted this fact in 1995.[12] Author Wei Jincheng followed up on this thought in 1996 adding that a People's War with an IW context can be

> ...carried out by hundreds of millions of people using open-type modern information systems. Because the traditional mode of industrial production has changed from centralization to dispersion, and commercial activities have expanded from urban areas to rural areas, the working method and mode of interaction in the original sense are increasingly information-based...the chance of the people taking the initiative and randomly participating in the war increased.[13]

Some believe electronics, computer, and information engineering experts are likely to become the genuine heroes of a new People's War much like the warrior class of the past.[14] Perhaps this focus explains why, in addition to economic factors, China is willing to reduce the size of its army. China believes it can keep up with other countries by utilizing a multitude of information engineers and citizens with laptops instead of just soldiers. China clearly has the people to conduct "take home battle," a reference to electronic battles conducted with laptops at home. The problem is how to identify and train the force, put enough quality Chinese-based equipment in their hands, and find more information space for all of these people.[15]

The integration of civilians with the military also implies networking. In a newspaper article in August 2000 entitled "PRC Army Pays Attention to the Role of Network Warfare," the author stated:

> Some military figures noted that the people's war has undergone an epochal leap from the support-the-front army that made its advances on vehicles to the

---

[11] Li Yinnina, in Huang Youfu, Zhang Bibo, and Hang Song, "New Subjects of Study Brought about by Information War—Summary of Army Command Academy Seminar on 'Confrontation of Command on Information Battlefield" Jiefangjun Bao (Liberation Army Daily), 11 November 1997, p. 6 as translated and reported in FBIS-CHI-97-354, insert date 23 December 1997(at this time FBIS was in hard copy, therefore it was not "downloaded from" but rather "reported in."

[12] Wang Pufeng, "Meeting the Challenge of Information Warfare," Zhongguo Junshi Kexue (China Military Science), 20 February 1995, Number 1, pp. 8-18 as translated and reported in FBIS-CHI-95-129, 6 July 1995, pp. 29-30.

[13] Wei Jincheng, "New Form of People's Warfare," Jiefangjun Bao (Liberation Army Daily), 11 June 1996, p. 6 as translated and reported in FBIS-CHI-96-159, insert date 16 August 1996.

[14] Shen Weiguang, "Focus of Contemporary World Military Revolution—Introduction to Research in IW," Jiefangjun Bao, 7 November 1995 , p. 6 as translated and reported in FBIS-CHI-95-239, 13 December 1995, pp. 22-27.

[15] Wang Xiaodong, "Special Means of Warfare in the Information Age: Strategic Information Warfare," Jianchuan Zhishi, 30 June 1999 as translated and downloaded from the FBIS Web site on 27 July 1999.

contemporary network warfare 'on keyboards.' . . . Jiefangjun Bao (Liberation Army Daily) [the Chinese Armed Forces newspaper also called the PLA Daily] maintains that it is necessary to formulate rules and regulations regarding mobilization and preparation for "modern People's War" as well as information gathering and processing, online offensives and defenses, network technology research and exchanges, and so on in order to provide the norms for the orderly preparation and building of a "network People's War."[16]

IW specialist Shen Weiguang wrote that combatants can be soldiers or a teenager, whoever possesses the weapon called a computer. The whole of society will replace traditional battlefields as different classes and social groups take part in political activities within their own countries. He advocated developing information protection troops composed of scientists, police, soldiers, and other experts versed in IW to safeguard the security of the national information boundary and to launch counterattacks against an information invasion by other countries.[17] Other analysts believe the goal of Chinese doctrine is to unify the concept of People's War with the concept of victory through information.[18]

Chinese analysts have witnessed this tendency to integrate civilians into the IW battle in other countries and are keen to point out the increased role of society in foreign IW scenarios. Wang Xiaodong, while analyzing a US RAND Corporation IW document, observed that the study unknowingly outlined a People's War in the information age. This was because the authors of the RAND study went back to the day before the IW assault to analyze what could have been done by society (the "People") for protection. He stated:

Even as the government mobilized troops, the numbers and roles of traditional warriors will be sharply less than those of technical experts in all lines . . . since thousands of personal computers can be linked up to perform a common operation, to perform many tasks in place of a large-scale military computer, an IW victory will very likely be determined by which side can mobilize the most computer experts and part-time fans. That will be a real People's War . . . .[19]

As noted above, a modern People's War requires close civil-military technological integration. In September 2000, some two weeks before the release of the Chinese Defense White Paper, the PLA Daily released an article on China's military telecommunication (telecom) developments that was indicative of such integration. The article noted that in 1991, Chairman Jiang Zemin called for building common telecommunication systems for military and civilian use to meet peacetime and wartime needs. Only in such fashion could military telecommunications catch up with its civilian

---

[16] "PRC Army Pays Attention to the Role of Network Warfare," Hong Kong Zhongguo Tongxun She, 0947 GMT, 6 August 2000, as translated and downloaded from the FBIS Web site on 6 August 2000.
[17] Shen, "Checking Information Warfare-Epoch Mission of Intellectual Military."
[18] Yang Shuqi and Guo Ruobing, [no title provided], Zhongguo Guofang Keji X, September-December 1996, Number 5/6, pp. 90-93 as translated and reported in FBIS-CHI-98-029, insert date 30 January 1998.
[19] Ibid.

8

counterpart. One way to do this was to create reserve forces (a key component uniting civilian and military sectors in a People's War) with telecommunications, IW, and information operations (IO) missions. The paper noted:

> We have built a reserve telecom force structure with a reserve telecom regiment as the backbone, with an information industrial department as the base. . . have built a reserve contingent of qualified high-tech telecom and transmission personnel with those specializing in satellite telecoms, relay telecoms, digital telecoms, telegraph (telephone) telecoms, and optical-fiber telecoms as the main force . . . and have built a contingent of highly qualified personnel with computer experts, network monitoring experts, as well as radio telecom units serving as the backbone.[20]

This emphasis indicates that China's IW reserve forces have become one of the important high-tech links in the country's People's War and local-war theories. The reserve forces supporting a People's War in the past were used to support PLA forces in the event of a foreign intervention in China. Today's reserve forces are capable of doing something even the PLA was unable to do for many years—reaching enemy forces or financial institutions continents away with electronic and information weapons. Some electronic attacks, if properly targeted, could theoretically be as devastating to a country's economy as the damage inflicted by an intercontinental missile.

Ideas for uniting a People's War with IW found fertile ground in the 1.5 million-reserve force of China. The People's Liberation Army is turning reserve forces in some districts into mini-IW regiments. For example, in the Echeng District (about seven hundred miles due south of Beijing) in Hubei Province, the People's Armed Forces Department (PAFD) reportedly organized twenty city departments (telecommunications, power, finance, TV, medical, and so on) into a militia/reserve IW regiment. The PAFD had a network-warfare battalion, as well as electronic-warfare (EW), intelligence, and PSYWAR battalions, and thirty-five technical "Fenduis" (squad to battalion). The PAFD also set up the first reserve IW training base for five hundred people. Instructors at the base have reportedly run an "Informaticized People's Warfare Network Simulation Exercise." Even a Web site was given for the Echeng District PAFD, http://ezarmy.net.[21]

On 27 June of 2000, the city of Ezhou (also in Hubei Province of the Echeng District) carried out a national defense mobilization exercise via computer networks. The initial mission, according to Zhu Jianjian, commander of the military sub-district, was to explore how civil networks could be used in wartime and how networks could be used for rapid mobilization in order to improve the quality and efficiency of national defense mobilization work. A second mission was to recruit technical soldiers and scientific and technological equipment from the national defense mobilization database. An additional

---

[20] Zhang Fuyou, "With Joint Efforts Made by Army and People, Military Telecommunications Makes Leap Forward," Jiefangjun Bao (Liberation Army Daily), 27 September 2000, as translated and downloaded from FBIS Web site on 27 September 2000.
[21] China National Defense News, 24 January 2000, provided by Mr. William Belk via e-mail. Mr. Belk is the head of a skilled US reservist group that studies China.

task was to establish wartime command organs and to formulate various preliminary plans. During the exercise, networks of the command center and the member units of the city's national defense mobilization committee were linked in order to transmit audio and video information to each other. Cable TV and computer networks were integrated and put to use.[22]

Echeng is not the only district with reserve/militia units conducting IW training. The Fujan Province, according to a published report, held a meeting at Xiamen in December 1999 that utilized reserve and militia forces. The report cited militia high-technology Fenduis that carried out electronic countermeasures and network attack, defense, and radar-reconnaissance operations. These operations were conducted as part of an enforced blockade of an island. The Xiamen area is a special economic zone and attracts a higher than usual number of science and technology clients to the area.[23] Thus it is a prime area for IW related activities.

There are also reports of reserve IW activity in Xian PAFD and in the Datong military sub-district. In Xian, the PAFD IW Fendui acted as opposing forces (OPFOR) for a military district exercise in the Jinan Military Region. Ten IO methods were listed: planting information mines, conducting information reconnaissance, changing network data, releasing information bombs, dumping information garbage, disseminating propaganda, applying information deception, releasing clone information, organizing information defense, and establishing network spy stations.[24] In Datong, more than forty members of a high-tech unit focused on information security and on seizing partial network domination in network warfare. The unit held three network warfare OPFOR demonstrations for the Beijing Military Region, the Central Military Commission, the General Staff, and North China PLA units.[25]

The PLA and reserve forces also reportedly have their own Web sites and simulation centers. China now has some four hundred military Web sites, according to one report. Examples are Xinhua Net's Junshi Tiandi (Military Sphere), Zhongxin Net's Junshi Tiandi (Military Sphere), Zhong Qing Zaixian's military section Zhong Qing Fenghuo (China Youth Beacon) available at China Youth Online (www.cyol.net), Jiefangjun Bao (Liberation Army Daily), and Jiefang Huabao (www.plapic.con.cn or PLA pictorial of the Academy of Military Sciences).[26] On 7 January 2001 several unidentified companies agreed to form the China C-Net Strategic Alliance, a second-generation, Internet-like network for China's government and industry. No start dates for construction or completion were offered. The Xinhua News Agency release noted, "the current one [Internet] has too many faults and is incapable of satisfying the needs of the Chinese government and companies as they enter the digital age." It is unknown whether

---

[22] Xu Jiwu and Xiao Xinmin, "Civil Networks Used in War," Jiefangjun Bao (Liberation Army Daily) (Internet version-www) in Chinese, 1 July 2000, p. 2 as translated and downloaded from FBIS Web site on 3 July 2000.
[23] China National Defense News, 15 December 1999, p. 1, provided by Mr. Belk via e-mail.
[24] Qianjin Bao, 10 December 1999, provided by Mr. Belk via e-mail.
[25] China National Defense News, 26 January 2000, provided by Mr. Belk via e-mail.
[26] Wei Kaqing, "On the Sudden Emergence of Military Web Sites," Zhongguo Guofang Bao, 6 November 2000, p. 4 as translated and downloaded from the FBIS Web site on 14 December 2000.

foreigners will have access to the new net or if it will be compatible with the existing Internet.[27]

A theoretical competitor to IW in this time of transition for many armies is knowledge warfare. Knowledge warfare to the Chinese refers to a battle of competing brains (decision-makers on both sides of a confrontation) that process seemingly endless streams of information (the IW connection) and regurgitate the information in intelligible, useable form giving one side an advantage. Innovation and the ability to "think outside the box" are also important. The speed of both innovation and processing thus determines combat power.[28] A commander must be able to think in terms other than two-dimensional maps, telephones, and so on. How to think may be more important than how to do something. Some believe that the losers in future war will be those lacking command thinking rather than backward technology.[29] The confrontation of two commands is a type of knowledge war that involves a trial of strength revolving around the procurement, control, and use of information,[30] thus making intellectual resources as important as scarce material resources. Knowledge becomes the paramount strategic resource, more important in the balance of power than weapons. According to some sources, warfare may be waged around the struggle for intellectual resources, such as the allegiance of a high-tech expert or the patented right to a piece of technology.[31]

Chinese IW Definitions: Focus on Network and Cognitive Processes

The definition of information war and information operations is under constant revision in the US, and, for that reason, it is not surprising that Chinese definitions continue to evolve over time. For comparative purposes for the remainder of this section, the US Armed Forces' definitions of IO and IW are presented here.

The 1998 Joint Publication 3-13, <u>Joint Doctrine for Information Operations</u>, and the <u>Department of Defense Dictionary of Military and Related Terms</u> (the latter last updated on 5 June 2003) both defined information operations as "actions taken to affect adversary information and information systems, while defending one's own information and information systems (major capabilities to conduct IO include, but are not limited to, OPSEC, PSYOP, military deception, EW, and physical attack/destruction, and could include computer network attack)." Both publications defined IW as "information operations conducted during time of crisis or conflict to achieve or promote specific objectives over a specific adversary or adversaries."[32]

[27] Beijing, <u>The Associated Press</u>, 8 January 2001,
[28] Zhang Guoyu, "Symposium on Challenge of Knowledge Revolution for the Military," <u>Jiefangjun Bao</u> (<u>Liberation Army Daily</u>), 5 January 1999, p. 6 as translated and downloaded from the FBIS Web site on 27 January 1999.
[29] Shen, "Focus of Contemporary World Military Revolution—Introduction to research in IW."
[30] Li Yinnina, et. al.
[31] Cui Yonggui, in Zhang Guoyu's "Symposium on Challenge of Knowledge Revolution for the Military," <u>Jiefangjun Bao</u> (<u>Liberation Army Daily</u>), 5 January 1999, p. 6 as translated and downloaded from the FBIS Web site on 27 January 1999.
[32] <u>Joint Pub 3-13, Joint Doctrine for Information Operations</u>, 9 October 1998, p. I-9, I-11..

To demonstrate the ongoing changes in US definitions, consider the following. The US Army, in its latest release of the corresponding field manual on information operations, FM 3-13, in November 2003 defined information operations as

The employment of the core capabilities of electronic warfare, computer network operations, psychological operations, military deception, and operations security, in concert with specified supporting and related capabilities, to affect or defend information and information systems, and to influence decision-making.[33]

The US Army no longer defined information war in its new FM 3-13.

The source for Chinese definitions is different than that for US definitions. There are no field manuals with officially accepted definitions that one can draw upon. Instead, analysts must rely on the work of area specialists who occupy key posts in the military or on creative thinkers who may develop concepts outside the military's official scope. There are several Chinese authors who command respect for the breadth of their works and depth of their thought on IW issues: Dr. Shen Weiguang, Major General Wang Pufeng, Major General Wang Baocun, General Yuan Banggen, and Major General Dai Qingmin (for more on Dai, see Chapter Three).

Studying Chinese IW definitions consecutively by year offers clues to the developing nature of Chinese IW theory. Shen stated in 1996 that the definition of IW is a war in which both sides strive to hold the battlefield initiative by controlling the flow of information and intelligence. This initial definition did not address information superiority or information operations, just information control. (Shen's emphasis on control will also be discussed in Chapter Three.) Instead of protecting friendly information systems and attacking enemy systems, as the US defines the term, Shen emphasized protecting oneself and controlling the enemy. [34] Wang Pufeng, also writing in 1996, stated that the central issue in achieving victory in IW is control of information. Authors Yang Shuqi and Guo Ruobing added their voices to this emphasis on control, stating that the most important initiative on future battlefields would be the power to control information. The side that has the capability to control information resources and utilization will win. They wrote that these are the indices of a nation's capacity to direct a war effort.[35] Thus, in 1996 the emphasis was clearly on control.

In 1997 there were fewer attempts to define IW. Author Liang Zhenxing stated that IW includes all types of war-fighting activities that involve the exploitation, alteration, and paralysis of the enemy's information and information systems, as well as all those types of activities that involve protecting one's own information and information systems from exploitation, alteration, and paralysis by the enemy. Liang added that the Chinese definition of IW should take into consideration Chinese characteristics, but

---

[33] Information Operations: Doctrine, Tactics, Techniques, and Procedures, FM 3-13, November 2003, p. 1-13.
[34] Shen Weiguang, [no title provided], Zhongguo Guofang Keji X, September-December 1996, Number 5/6, pp. 87-89 as translated and reported in FBIS-CHI-98-029, insert date 30 January 1998.
[35] Yang Shuqi and Guo Ruobing.

should also be in line with the prevailing international definition. Perhaps for that reason his IW definition is closer than some to the US definition. Liang added that the essence of IW is to render the operational space unclear and indistinct to the enemy while making it transparent to one's own forces.[36]

In 1997 another author, then Senior Colonel Wang Baocun, provided a masterful description of IW through the dissecting eyes of Chinese military science. His article covered the forms, nature, levels, distinctions, features and principles of IW. He listed:

Forms of IW: peacetime, crisis and wartime
Nature of IW: offensive and defensive operations
Levels of IW: national, strategic, theater, and tactical
Other Distinctions of IW: command and control, intelligence, electronic, psychological, cyberspace, hackers, virtual, economic, strategy, and precision
Features of IW: complexity, limited goals, short duration, less damage, larger battle space and less troop density, transparency, the intense struggle for information superiority, increased integration, increased demand on command, new aspects of massing forces, and the fact that effective strength may not be the main target
Principles of IW: decapitation, blinding, transparency, quick response, and survival.[37]

In 1998 there were even fewer original discussions of the term IW. One analyst defined IW as the ability to hinder an opponent's decision-making while protecting friendly decision-making abilities. It is interesting that the Chinese emphasis was not on attacking enemy information or information systems but on "hindering" an opponent's decision making.[38] It is a slight but significant diversion from the US definition.

In 1999 Chinese analysts again returned to a serious debate over IW issues. This time Shen defined IW more broadly as involving two sides in pitched battle against one another in the political, economic, cultural, scientific, social, and technological fields. The fight was over information space and resources. He also defined IW narrowly as the confrontation of warring parties in the field of information. The essence of IW, Shen wrote, is to attain the objective of "forcing enemy troops to surrender without a fight" through the use of information superiority.[39] Obviously this definition echoes historical Chinese thoughts on warfare. However, this seems to imply that information superiority is more of a cognitive than systems related process.

---

[36] Liang Zhexing, [no title offered], Zhongguo Dianzi Bao [China Electronics News], speech presented 15 September 1997 but printed on 24 October 1998, as translated and reported in FBIS-CHI-98-012, insert date 13 January 1998.

[37] Wang Baocun, "A Preliminary Analysis of IW," Zhongguo Junshi Kexue, Number 4, 20 November 1997, pp. 102-111 as translated and downloaded from the FBIS Web site on 20 November 1997.

[38] Wang Jianghuai and Lin Dong, "Viewing Our Army's Quality Building from the Perspective of What Information Warfare Demands," Jiefangjun Bao (Liberation Army Daily), 3 March 1998, p. 6 as translated and downloaded from the FBIS Web site on 16 March 1998.

[39] Shen, "Checking Information Warfare-Epoch Mission of Intellectual Military."

Another Chinese author who defined IW in 1999 was Yuan Banggen, the head of a General Staff Directorate. He stated that IW is the struggle waged to seize and keep control over information, and the struggle between belligerent parties to seize the initiative in acquiring, controlling and using information. Capitalizing on and sabotaging the enemy's information resources, information system, and informationized-weapon systems helps accomplish this, as well as utilizing and protecting one's own information resources, information systems, and informationized-weapon systems. Yuan thus substitutes capitalizing and sabotaging for the US term "attacking" while simultaneously emphasizing control. He also noted that IW is a kind of knowledge warfare, a rivalry between groups of professionals with high-tech knowledge.[40]

In 1999 General Wang Baocun added more to the IW discussion. He distinguished between IW and informationized war. He defined IW as a form of fighting and part of a complete war while defining informationized warfare as an entirely new form of war. IW would gradually become informationized war, Wang noted, but this won't happen until the middle of the twenty-first century when informationized forces will be available. The latter is the follow-on to mechanized forces. Wang views informationized forces as the soul of Sun Tsu's "subduing the enemy without battle," a tactic requiring superior military strength, full preparedness, destruction of the enemy's strategy, and the ability to cultivate, conduct and foster discipline. The goals are to "force the enemy side to regard their goal as our goal" and to "force the opponent to give up the will to resist and end the confrontation and stop fighting by attacking an enemy's perception and belief via information energy." If perceptions are attacked correctly, morale drops and, with it, control, one of the main ingredients of IW. The proper information assault can make this work.[41] Wang's discussion thus includes some cognitive aspects of IW and again an emphasis on control.

Xie Guang, the Vice-Minister of the Commission of Science, Technology and Industry for National Defense at the time, also defined IW in December 1999. He stated that IW

> . . . in the military sense means overall use of various types of information techniques, equipment, and systems, using disturbance, misinformation or destruction of the enemy's information systems, particularly his command systems, to shake the determination of the enemy's policymakers, and at the same time the use of all means possible to ensure that one's own information systems are not damaged or disturbed.[42]

China's external IW goal is thus to shake the determination of opposing policymakers, while its internal goal is to protect information systems. Xie described the three areas of IW as:

---

[40] Yuan Banggen, "On IW, Digital Battlefields," Zhongguo Junshi Kexue, 20 February 1999, pp. 46-51 as translated and downloaded from the FBIS Web site on 17 July 1999.
[41] Wang Baocun.
[42] Xie Guang," Wars under High-Tech," Renmin Ribao, 27 December 1999, p. 7 as translated and downloaded from the FBIS Web site on 30 January 1999.

First–control, communications, computers, intelligence, surveillance and reconnaissance (C4ISR)
Second–electronic warfare
Third–computer attack and defense methods.

In 2000, Wang Pufeng offered a deeper explanation of information war than any seen to date, distinguishing it from information warfare. In Wang's opinion, an information war refers to a kind of war and a kind of war pattern, while information warfare refers to a kind of operation and a kind of operational pattern. The new operational pattern refers to operations in a computer-network space. Information warfare embraces information-detection systems, information-transmission systems, information and weapon-strike systems, and information-processing and use systems. Information war thus embraces information warfare. Both integrate information and energy and use an information-network-based battlefield as their arena of activity.[43]

Other than Wang Pufeng, there were very few Chinese authors who attempted to define information operations. One who did was Yuan Banggen in his 1999 article. He stated that information operations are specific IW operations. IW is the core of informationized warfare, whereas information operations are the manifestation of information warfare on the battlefield. IO means information wars in the narrow sense, that is the military field, and they are usually integrated, new technology countermeasures in Yuan's opinion. IO's theoretical system is formed from two levels: basic and application. Basic theories consist of basic concepts about IO such as its organizational structure and technological equipment, command and control for IO, and so on. Application theories can be categorized into offensive IO and defensive IO; strategic, operational, campaign and tactical levels; and into peacetime, wartime, and crisis-period IO. All activities of IO focus attention on command and control. IO's two missions are preparation and implementation. Its principles are centralized command, multilevel power delegation, multidimensional inspection and testing, timely decision making, and the integration of military and civilian actions with a focus on key links.[44]

Yuan also discussed digital forces and digital battlefields in the same article. Digital forces are new-generation combat units. These forces are mainly armed with digitized electronic-information equipment and combat weapons. They are characterized by the integration of command and control, intelligence, reconnaissance, early warning, detection, communications, electronic countermeasures, and the intellectualization of principal combat weapons. The digital battlefield denotes the battlefield where the effective linking and use of strategic, campaign, and tactical command-automation systems are realized based on digital-information technology. Digital forces and digital battlefields are the two main components of IW. Digital forces can also be called informationized forces and digital battlefields can also be called informationized

---

[43] Wang Pufeng, [no title provided], Hong Kong Hsien-Tai Chun-Shih (Conmilit), 11 April 2000, pp. 19-21 as translated and downloaded from the FBIS Web site on 3 May 2000.
[44] Yuan Banggen.

battlefields.[45] The digitization standard of the communication system affects and determines the quality and process of the construction of digital forces and digital battlefields. Therefore, the construction of the digitized communication system is the "core of cores" in the construction of digital forces and digital battlefields.[46]

Another IW concept is information-network warfare (INW). Cui Yonggui broadly defined it as a war in which two opposing sides try to take over information space and vie for information resources. Narrowly defined, INW refers to a confrontation on the network between two opposing sides in war. INW tests human willpower, intelligence, and technology.[47] Another author, Qi Jianguo, recommended that the PLA establish an authoritative, centralized, and united network People's War organ. It would control information operations and networking activities, and it would allow for the conduct of mobilization exercises and education on People's War on the net. Similar organs would be established at different levels in the provinces, cities, and prefectures. Laws and regulations would need to be formulated in order to standardize the preparation and development of a network People's War.[48] It was noted that China must uphold the principle of combining the establishment of networks for both wartime and peacetime use, setting up networks for both military and civilian use, and developing Internet service in a limited manner.[49]

Finally, Wang Baocun wrote another article in 2000 in which he redefined IW from his previous outline in 1997. In "The Current Revolution in Military Affairs and its Impact on Asia-Pacific Security," Wang's article (the only one to appear in English in the journal, thus intended for Western audiences) reflected a Western view of IW and the Revolution in Military Affairs (RMA). He defines IW as "a form of combat actions that attacks the information and information systems of the enemy while protecting the information and information systems of one's own side." Wang added that the contents of IW are military security, military deception, physical attack, electronic warfare, psychological warfare and net warfare, and that its basic purpose is to seize and maintain information dominance.[50] Wang thus revised the definition of IW he offered in 1997. His new definition sounded very much like the US definition that was developed in 1998.

High-tech war and information war articles were published in the main journal of the Chinese Academy of Military Science, China Military Science. China Military Science approximates in importance to the US journal Joint Forces Quarterly. No fewer than six articles discussed high-tech war, and four covered IW in 1999. In 2000 four articles discussed high-tech war, and five discussed IW.

---

[45] Ibid.
[46] Ibid.
[47] Cui Yonggui.
[48] Qi Jianguo, "Thought on Internet War," Jiefangjun Bao (Liberation Army Daily), Internet version, 16 May 2000, p. 6 as translated and downloaded from the FBIS Web site on 16 May 2000.
[49] Ibid.
[50] Wang Baocun, "The Current Revolution in Military Affairs and its Impact on Asia-Pacific Security," China Military Science, Number 4, 2000, p. 139.

While most of the definitions above focused principally on systems, there was also a Chinese predilection to study cognitive processes. In fact some, like Shen, believe that IW's essence is the sum of information capabilities to break the enemy's will to resist by attacking his cognitive understanding and convictions causing the enemy to give up all resistance and terminate the war. Shen noted in 1996 the main tasks of IW are disrupting the enemy's cognitive system and trust system.[51]

Wang Baocun also believes strongly in the union of IW and cognitive processes. In one of his articles he described perception structures, perception systems, and belief systems as IW components. He defined a perception structure as "all things that an individual or a group considers correct or true, regardless of whether these things that are considered correct or true have been obtained through perception or belief." Perception structures are composed of perception systems. These systems "are established and operated in order to understand or observe verifiable phenomena by turning such phenomena into perceptible realities and subsequently to make decisions or take action on the basis of intuitive understanding of such realities." Belief systems are "systems which guide testable empirical information and such information and consciousness that cannot be tested or are hard to test."[52]

This focus on perceptions and beliefs is interesting because some Chinese IW specialists believe that communications and the media are the main areas of IW concern today. According to Yang Minqing, IW is a face-off in the field of information between opposing parties. This is reflected primarily in a fight to gain the initiative over information resources and control of the production, transmission, and processing of information so as to damage information-based, public opinion on the enemy's side. Yang believes that IW is divided into two fields. They are national IW (which tries to seize information by intelligence, diplomacy, commercial, and strategic psychological warfare) and national defense IW (which tries to maintain an upper hand over information acquisition between two armies, and includes intelligence, electronic, command and control, and psychological warfare). In both cases the fight is over information space and information resources. A point of IW concern is communications/media, which can play a strategic role. Communications can also have a deterrent effect, and can possess an ability to manipulate the populace, wherein lies its importance as a target.[53]

Computer Confrontation

There apparently was considerable work accomplished in the PLA between 1995 and 2000 in the field of military computer operations. The PLA appears to equate computer network operations with the term computer confrontation operations. The 1999 book Information Warfare stated

---

[51] Shen Weiguang, [no title provided], Zhongguo Guofang Keji X, September-December 1996.

[52] Wang Baocun, "New Military Revolution in the World, 'Subduing Enemy Force without Battle' and Informationized Warfare," Zhongguo Junshi Kexue (China Military Science), 4 May 1999, pp. 60-63 as translated and downloaded from the FBIS Web site on 23 August 1999.

[53] Yang Minqing, "Facing Future Information War," Jingji Cankao Bao, 15 October 1999, p. 5 as translated and downloaded from the FBIS Web site on 29 November 1999.

There will be point-to-point confrontation between computers as well as theater-to-theater confrontation. There will be wireless confrontation as well as confrontation via cables…there will be wartime confrontation as well as confrontation in peacetime. There will be confrontation between military computers as well as between civilian computers. [54]

Computer confrontation has been referred to as a series of confrontational activities between two sides that focus on the use and activities of computer information systems. Computer information system confrontation includes hardware and software confrontation, electromagnetic and virus confrontation, network and hacker confrontation, and confrontations among and between military and civilian systems. Computer confrontation must be coordinated with communications confrontation, electronic confrontation, radar confrontation, and so on to facilitate joint operations. China can train for a single form and method or multiple forms and methods of confrontation based on specific conditions, targets, and stages.[55] Since this book was published in 1999, it is clear that such operations had been ongoing for at least a few years prior.

Computer confrontation also occupies a key spot in information warfare campaign planning. One of the goals of IW is to maintain China's ability to command and control. At critical times and in the region related to the overall campaign operation, IW must cut off the enemy's ability to get, control, and use information and to influence, reduce, and even destroy the enemy's capabilities to observe, make decisions, and command and control troops.[56] This enables not only information superiority, but also strategic and campaign superiority, and it creates conditions for winning a decisive battle. The first targets of a campaign, according to Information War, are information systems of detection, command, and telecommunication. This enables a force to take away or reduce an enemy's ability to control information and create conditions for the later use of forces and firepower. IW activities are run throughout the entire campaign operation.[57]

Chinese Organizations and Training to Conduct IW

There are several organizations charged with IW instruction for the PLA. The lead organization is the Communications Command Academy. The Academy is located in Wuhan, the capital of central China's Hubei Province. In 1998 the Academy announced the publication of two books, Command and Control in IW and Technology in IW that became the leading Chinese IW texts. The first book discussed who should exercise command and control (C2); the means to exercise C2; the spheres, principles and forms of IO; new concepts for building an information corps; and the principles on which IW should be based. The second book explored the composition, characteristics, and development trends of basic IW technologies. This included the retrieval, transmission and processing of information. It also established a structural system for IW and offered

---

[54] "Computer Confrontation," Information Warfare, Chapter Five, January 1999.
[55] Ibid.
[56] Information about IW campaign planning was taken from On Military Campaigns, May 2000, translation provided to the author by FBIS.
[57] Ibid.

strategies for technological developments in the army. The Academy is well respected for its IW curriculum that analyzes strategic, operational, and tactical IW requirements.[58] Nearly two years later, the Communications Command Academy hosted a training course on information war, research on information command and tactics, and research on information combat.[59] Interestingly, the academy is located not far from the reserve component IW regiment in Echeng district.

A second leading PLA IW institute is the Information Engineering University, established by combining the Institute of Information Engineering, the Electronic Technology College, and the Survey and Mapping College. The university is located in Zhengzhou, the capital of Henan Province. According to its President, Major General Zhou Rongting, it will help cultivate professionals for high-tech warfare involving the use of information and will create a number of new specialties such as remote-image-information engineering, satellite-navigation and positioning engineering, and map data banks. Major specialties include information security, communications technology, and space technology.[60]

A third PLA IW location is the Science and Engineering University. It was established by combining the Institute of Communications Engineering, the Engineering Institute of the Engineering Corps, the Meteorology Institute of the Air Force, and the 63rd Research Institute of the General Staff headquarters. It trains new military personnel in fields such as IW, communication and command automation, and other subjects.[61] University President Major General Si Laiyi said that a new Institute of Computer and Command Automation set up six disciplines, including electronic engineering, information engineering, network engineering, command-automation engineering, and counterinformation with key information-warfare technologies as the core. There are over four hundred experts and professors at the university teaching IW theories and technological subjects.[62]

A fourth PLA IW institute is the National Defense Science and Technology University in Changsha. Directly under the supervision of the Central Military Commission, it is where the "Yin He" series of supercomputers are developed.[63] From April to June 1999 some sixty senior officers (average age 53) studied high-tech warfare at the university while the war over Kosovo was raging. Lessons included reconnaissance, monitoring technology, precision-guidance technology, electronic war,

[58] Lei Yuanshen, "New Breakthrough in the Study of Information Warfare," Jiefangjun Bao (Liberation Army Daily), 21 July 1998 p. 6 as translated and downloaded from the FBIS Web site on 12 August 1998.
[59] "Chinese Military Holds Training Course on Information War," Xinhua, 22 May 2000 as translated and downloaded from the FBIS Web site on 22 May 2000.
[60] "University to Foster Talent for High-Tech Warfare," Xinhua, 17 November 1999 as translated and downloaded from the FBIS Web site on 17 November 1999.
[61] Ma Xiaochun, "PLA Sets Up Four New Academies," Xinhua, 2 July 1999 as translated and downloaded from the FBIS Web site on 7 July 1999.
[62] "PLA Trains Personnel for Information Warfare," Hong Kong Tai Yang Pao 15 September 1999, p. A17 as translated and downloaded from the FBIS Web site on 15 September 1999.
[63] Guo Hao, "Chinese Military Prepares to Fight Digital Warfare," Hong Kong Kuang Chiao Ching, 16 March, 2000, Number 330, pp. 19-21 as translated and downloaded from the FBIS Web site on 16 March 2000.

and information war, among other subjects. One conclusion about future wars was that "an information umbrella has become the most important factor, and the opponent's nerve center the most important military target."[64] The university apparently runs this course several times a year at army level and above army levels.[65] Nearly three hundred officers had received training at the university by April 2000. Special emphasis in one class was placed on instruction and discussion of electronic and information techniques (and associated topics, such as guidance control, command automation, etc.) and "three offenses and three defenses" training (see discussion below in this section).[66]

A PLA Navy institute that studies and teaches IW subjects is the Navy Engineering College headed by President Shao Zijun. The general orientation of the College is to combine arms and information by integrating electronic information with weapons systems. The College hopes to help adapt the Chinese navy to the combat needs of information warfare. The College is also located in Wuhan and perhaps shares research on IW with the Communications Command Academy.[67]

These universities and colleges reflect the IW changes that the PLA foresees. Information is viewed as a multiplier of combat effectiveness and a strategic resource. In the opinion of some instructors, warfare is now about intelligence and resourcefulness, new temporal-spatial concepts, resolute decisiveness, and the "soft science" technology located in new weapons.[68] These forms and means of warfare present significant challenges to Chinese cadres assigned to teach these subjects since the level of science skills among commanders is inadequate. The system of training advanced in 1996 to handle this problem involved first laying a sound strategic foundation, then improving everyone's knowledge about IW by studying the experiences of foreign armies. These steps were to be followed by expanding basic IW skills, especially in electronic and psychological warfare, and in information attack and defense. Finally attention would be paid to converting knowledge to ability through the conduct of IW exercises. Press reports indicated that this plan was followed.[69] The first years were spent discussing the strategy and theory of the Revolution in Military Affairs and the use of IW in the Gulf War. A general discussion of the meaning and use of the offensive and defensive

---

[64] Xi Qixin and Zhao Yongxin, "Advancing toward High Technology—High Ranking Military Cadres Attending a Hi-Tech Training Course," Xinhua Domestic Service, 13 June 1999 as translated and downloaded from the FBIS Web site on 15 June 1999.

[65] Zhang Zhenzhong and Chang Jianguo, "Train Talented People at Different Levels for Information Warfare," Jiefangjun Bao (Liberation Army Daily), 2 February 1999, p. 6 as translated and downloaded from the FBIS Web site on 10 February 1999.

[66] Wang Wowen, "PRC Senior Military Cadres Trained on High Technology," Xinhua Domestic Service, 11 April 2000 as translated and downloaded from the FBIS Web site on 11 April 2000.

[67] "Shao Zijun Says the Navy Engineering College is Aimed at Developing New Naval Military Talent," Xinhua Hong Kong, 7 August 1999 as translated and downloaded from the FBIS Web site on 26 August 1999.

[68] Lei Zhuomin, "Information Warfare and Training of Skilled Commanders," Jiefangun Bao (Liberation Army Daily), 26 December 1995 p. 6 as translated and reported in FBIS document FBIS-CHI-96-036, 26 December 1995.

[69] Cheng Bingwen, "Let Training Lean Close to Information Warfare," Jiefangjun Bao (Liberation Army Daily), 12 November 1996 p. 6 as translated and reported in FBIS-CHI-96-230, inserted on 29 November 1996.

components of IW followed this. Finally, since 1997 numerous IW exercises were reported in the press.

One of the more interesting articles on IW training appeared in February 1999. IW was defined as knowledge-style warfare, a special trial of strength between highly talented people. This definition arose from the fact that high-tech war demands a high level of knowledge by commanders and operators, strong psychological qualities, command ability, and operational skills. Recognizing that China lags behind in several of these categories, the PLA leadership decided to carry out training at various levels. Each is age dependent. The first category is support-style talent, where the main targets are leading cadres who are over 40 years of age. These individuals are decision-makers, and the aim is to eliminate their information illiteracy, to change their concepts through training (from mechanized concepts to simulated-IW fighting), and to apply their new ideas to future war. The training content for this group is information technology basics, the theory of IW, and general knowledge of IW weapons. The training method is to focus on short training courses, supplemented by other methods.[70]

The second category is transitional-style talent. Here cadres aged 30-40 were targeted. As the future leaders of China, they must focus on enhancing their ability to command in IW environments. The training aims were to supply them with information-technology lessons they may have missed in college and to ensure they grasped the requirements, special features, and laws of future IW. It was also important for them to understand the components of information-weapons systems and to have instructors lay a firm foundation for information theory. Finally, they must master the principles, forms, methods, and skills for IW command.[71]

The third and final category is called regeneration-style talent. This involved cadres aged 30 or less. These individuals are already acclimated to an information society and possess a general, all-round foundation in modern information-technology theory. Their focus is on both command and technology. They receive advanced IW training, from ideological concepts to theoretical foundation to skill in application. They train for a longer period of time than the other two groups due to the breadth and depth of their instruction.[72]

The training for each age group includes:

- Basic theory, including computer basics and application, communications network technology, the information highway, and digitized units
- Electronic countermeasures and radar technology
- IW rules and regulations
- IW strategy and tactics
- Theater and strategic IW

---

[70] Zhang and Chang.
[71] Ibid.
[72] Ibid.

- Information systems, including gathering, handling, disseminating, and using information
- Combat command, monitoring, decision making, and control systems
- Information weapons, including concepts, principles of soft and hard destruction, and how to apply these weapons
- Simulated IW, protection of information systems, computer virus attacks and counterattacks, and jamming and counterjamming of communications networks.[73]

This article made it appear that China is well on its way to developing a first-rate, IW curriculum. But later reports suggest that this is still wishful thinking. For example, a July 1999 report noted the following:

> Irrationalities in the training content, system, and structure have kept IW training from truly becoming the mainstream of our military training. At present, IW training is in a "do-as-you-please" situation in which the content is not systematic, the operations lack order, there are no assessment standards, and management lacks regulations.[74]

The requirement to fulfill many of these points was reemphasized in October 1999 by Fu Quanyou, Chief of the Chinese General Staff at the time. He wrote that four new aspects must be created. These were to create new IW theories, design a modern system of high-tech military training, create high-tech military training forms and methods, and create operational, coordinating, and support training management mechanisms.[75]

There was much written about computer training in general, but very little about any specific aspect of training. There was, however, one exception. The 1999 book Information Warfare by Zhu and Chen mentioned previously had an outstanding chapter on IW training. These authors wrote that "computer confrontation training" assists not only operators but also the strategy making and organizational and command capabilities of commanders. The focus of Zhu and Chen was on the active defense. They discussed the need for offense through defense and the need to preempt in IW. Computer confrontation training included hardware and software, electromagnetic and virus confrontation, peacetime and wartime, and military versus civilian systems.[76]

Computer-confrontation training enhances a commander's capabilities for flexible adaptation. This enables great strategy, acute judgment, quick decision making, and organization. One must move from theory, to skills, to tactics, and then to real war according to the Chinese authors. Information should be provided according to tactical

---

[73] Ibid.
[74] Sun Haicheng, Yang Jie, and Zhang Guoyu, "Let Information Warfare Training Rule the Training Sites: Practice and Reflections from the First All-Army Collective Training Session for Division and Brigade Chiefs of Staff in Information Warfare Theory," Jiefangjun Bao (Liberation Army Daily), 13 July 1999 p. 6 as translated and downloaded from the FBIS Web site on 8 August 1999.
[75] Mao Xiaochun and Chen Hui, "Chief of Staff Fu Quanyuou on High-Tech Military Training," Xinhua Domestic Service, 0240 GMT, 16 October 1999 as translated and downloaded from the FBIS Web site on 16 October 1999.
[76] Zhu Wenguan and Chen Taiyi, Information Warfare, 1999, Chapter Five (Computer Operations).

principles and operational situations, and officers should analyze and judge important questions, content, and the main contradictions of a situation.[77] This type of computer training allows confrontation among participants. Further, the training should be based on operational tasks and joint exercises. This makes the training more real and offers participants a chance to analyze and judge operational situations and tactical principles. Offensive and defensive brigades are trained together, Information Warfare notes, making targets for one another. This allows participants to better grasp a basic knowledge of the role of computer confrontation to include its functions, characteristics, and use. Concentrated training includes:

- Computer system structure
- Network structure and protocol
- Basic principles of how computers work
- Basic tactics of computer confrontation
- Study of basic strategies and tactics of computer confrontation
- Focus on virus confrontation with electromagnetic and network confrontations being supplementary.[78]

Offensive training includes how to design viruses, organize virus invasions, control contagions, conduct electromagnetic jamming, decipher data and enter the other side's computer networks. Offensive brigades must repeatedly study and analyze the enemy's network structure, performance parameters, information characteristics, and electromagnetic standards. They must also be able to tell false from true information, be able to pinpoint enemy, computer-control centers, and be able to jam in targeted ways.[79]

A final item worthy of mention is the training style known as "striking at three things and defending against three things" which the Chinese claim has been upgraded to information-age standards. Old style "three-three" was centered on exhausting the enemy's vital forces, preserving China's vital forces, and striving for superiority in manpower, firepower, and machine power. The focal point of contention was to gain superiority in material capability. New style "three-three" is centered on obtaining, transmitting, handling, and protecting information. "Striking at three things" means countering enemy destruction by active offensive means to ensure the stability of China's information system. It also implies defending against precision attacks and is designed to obtain target information. Units at and above army level should focus their study on reconnaissance and early warning, command coordination, and application of strategy. Divisions and brigades should focus on studying the application of firepower and the improvement and innovation of hardware. Units at and below regimental level should study and train in how to "respond rapidly and hit accurately."[80]

---

[77] Ibid.

[78] Ibid.

[79] Ibid. At one point in the discussion, the authors state that "we need to observe our military's strategy of active offense and in computer confrontation training ensure both defense and offense are main partners…"

[80] Fan Changlong, "Stand in the Forefront of the New Military Revolution in Deepening Troop Training through Science and Technology," Jiefangjun Bao (Liberation Army Daily), 4 April 2000 p. 6 as translated and downloaded from the FBIS Web site on 6 April 2000.

"Defending against three things" means obtaining optical, infrared, and electromagnetic target information. The key lies in adopting various means to seal off and weaken information on the target's external radiation or making the enemy receive erroneous information. In addition, as students of dialectical materialism,[81] Chinese military scientists view IW developments through a "thesis" and "anti-thesis" dialectical framework and conduct much of their training and research in a similar fashion. They recommend conducting various types of "anti" training, such as anti-reconnaissance, anti-cruise missile, and anti-interference training to offset IW weaponry. They think in terms of establishing an anti-information battlefield monopoly in order to offset another nation's information superiority.

IW Exercises

There were several significant Chinese IW military exercises from 1997-2000. Each is important because exercises explain the transition from theory to practice. One of the first "special" PLA IW exercises took place in October 1997. In the Shenyang Military Region a Group Army (GA) underwent a computer attack that paralyzed its systems. The GA countered with virus-killing software, and the exercise was termed an "invasion and anti-invasion" event. This exercise involved the deployment of ground, logistics, medical, and air force units. As one observer noted:

> ...the speed of marking and mapping on the computer screens by the advisors was more than 20 times faster than the traditional manual methods, and accuracy was 100 percent [faster]. The computer network in the command unit was activating more than 100 terminals, connecting and commanding a fourth-degree campaign network...the commanders' attention was not on the number of documents handled, but on whether the high-tech design was excellent. Their focus was not on whether the commanding procedures and soldiers' movements were standardized, but on how much high technology was being applied to their strategies and operations.[82]

The Taiwan Central News Agency on 27 December 1997 published a report on the exercise and accused the PLA of using the exercise to develop a computer-virus warfare capability.[83]

In 1998, the Chinese offered another example of high-technology battlefield prowess when it staged an integrated high-technology exercise in October that united several military regions around the country. The center of gravity of the exercise was the Beijing Military Region where a joint defense warfare drill used a "military information

---

[81] Dialectical materialism was defined as "the Marxist theory that maintains the material basis of a reality constantly changing in a dialectical process and the priority of matter over mind." See the Merriam-Webster Online Dictionary, downloaded on 27 April 2004 from http://www/m-w/com/cgi-bin/dictionary?book. It has also been defined as "the doctrine of Karl Marx and Friedrich Engels, combining materialism with Hegel's logical dialectic in which conflict between two entities or forces, thesis and antithesis, is resolved by the formation of a new entity or force, the synthesis." Funk and Wagnalls Standard College Dictionary, Text Edition, Harcourt, Brace and World, Inc., 1968, p. 367.

[82] Xinhua, 1508 GMT, 22 October 1997, as translated and reported in the FBIS press.

[83] Taiwan Central News, 1057 GMT, 27 December 1997, as translated and reported in the FBIS press.

superhighway" for the first time. It was described as an information network sub-system of the command-automation system[84] that was composed of digital, dial, command net, and restricted channels. Other elements of the command-automation system are the command operations, audio and graphics process and control, and data encryption sub-systems. The exercise started on 20 October and was coordinated with several other regions. The superhighway transmitted graphics, characters, and audio data in addition to situation maps.[85]

The Lanzhou Military Region, which includes the Gobi Desert, most likely also participated since they reported on 26 October (as did the Beijing Region) of having participated in a high-technology exercise that emphasized electronic confrontation.[86] The focus of their effort was on electronic reconnaissance and counterreconnaissance, electronic interference and counter-interference, and electronic destruction and counterdestruction.[87] Earlier in October, the General Staff reported that it too had held an all-army, high-technology training exercise to discuss and design training issues to meet the challenges of the worldwide military revolution. Fu Quanyou, Chief of the General Staff at the time, attended and presided over the training exercise. Fu and the General Staff participants viewed the training of the Shenyang Military Region.[88] It is possible that this exercise may have been part of the Lanzhou and Beijing exercise mentioned above.

In October 1999, the PLA conducted another IW exercise. Two army groups of the Beijing Military Region conducted a confrontation campaign on the computer network. Reconnaissance and counterreconnaissance, interference and counterinterference, blocking and counterblocking, and air strikes and counter air strikes were practiced. Six categories were included in the software environment: resource sharing, command operations, situation displays, supplementary assessments, signal transmissions, and intelligence. A computer evaluation system analyzed the performance of the participants in a quantitative and qualitative manner. The Operations Department of the General Staff said this was the first time that a computer confrontation was

---

[84] In July 1999 a spokesman for a Theater of Operations stated that it had built the first theater command automation system. The system combines command, control, intelligence, communications countermeasures and joint command and management of Guangzhou functions to allow ground, naval and air forces to share information at the theater, army, division, and regimental levels. This "God of Field Operations" reportedly combines information processing with data facsimile, terminal processing, and GPS imaging. See "Guangzhou Theater of Operation Builds Army's First Command Automation System," Zhongguo Xinwen She, 26 July 1999 as translated and downloaded from the FBIS Web site on 10 August 1999.
[85] Xinhua Domestic Service, 1148 GMT, 26 October 1998, as translated and downloaded from the FBIS Web site on 26 October 1998.
[86] Ren Yanjun and Zhang Jianjun, "General Staff Department Holds All-Army Hi-Tech Training Exercise," Jiefangjun Bao (Liberation Army Daily), 2 October 1998, p. 1 as translated and downloaded from the FBIS Web site 2 October 1998.
[87] Zhongguo Xinwen She, 1309 GMT, 26 October 1998, as translated and downloaded from the FBIS Web site on 3 November 1998.
[88] Zhongguo Xinwen She, 1309 GMT, 26 October 1998, as translated and downloaded from the FBIS Web site on 26 October 1998.

conducted at the campaign level between a red army and a blue army.[89] Actual field operations of a similar nature (counterreconnaissance, etc.) were conducted simultaneously in the Jinan Theater. According to one observer, the performance of the high-tech weaponry was like that of a "tiger with wings."[90] The force demonstrated new tactics of using live ammunition to hit enemy cruise missiles and computer technology to hit information networks, links and points.[91] Advantages to using such high-tech tools, according to reporter Zhang Feng, are that it enables a near-real "war laboratory" experience. It improves the science and technology quality and strategic level of commanders and staff, helps to improve the capability of the trainee to command joint operations, and has a very high training quality and "benefit to cost" ratio.[92]

In July 2000, the Chengdu Military Region conducted a confrontational campaign exercise on the Internet. The three training tasks associated with the exercise included organizing and planning the campaign, striving for air and information control, and making and countering breakthroughs. Over one hundred terminals were linked for the exercise.[93] Three weeks later the Guangzhou Military Region conducted a high-tech exercise. An order to start controlling communications channels was sent out to the subordinate units who then "shouldered the major task of conducting information operations and giving electromagnetic wave support during future wars."[94]

In October 2000 an important training exercise was held in the Beijing Military District. CPC General Secretary Jiang Zemin attended this exhibition of scientific and technological prowess. One notable comment about the exercise was that the PLA had shifted its focus from its traditional "three strikes and three defenses (striking at tanks, aircraft, and airborne landings: defending against atomic, chemical, and biological weapons)" to a new "three strikes and three defenses (striking at stealth planes, cruise missiles, and armed helicopters: defending against precision strikes, electronic jamming, and reconnaissance surveillance)."[95] This change, different from the "three offenses and three defenses" described above, dramatized the shift from mechanized to information-based forces for many PLA members. The exercise reportedly put into use hundreds of

---

[89] Yang Hong and Zhou Meng, "Beijing Military Region Conducts Computer Exercise, Jiefangjun Bao (Liberation Army Daily), Internet version, 8 November 1999, as translated and downloaded from the FBIS Web site on 9 November 1999.

[90] Zhongguo Xinwen She, 1339 GMT, 6 November 1999, as translated and downloaded from the FBIS Web site on 9 November 1999.

[91] Xinhua Domestic Service, 0905 GMT, 15 October 1999 as translated and downloaded from the FBIS Web site on 15 October 1999.

[92] Zhang Feng, "The Chinese Armed Forces Advance toward the Virtual Battlefield…," Jiefangjun Bao (Liberation Army Daily), 24 November 1999, p. 5 as translated and downloaded from the FBIS Web site on 24 November 1999.

[93] Xu Wenliang and Wan Yuan, "Chengdu Military Region Conducts Long-Range Confrontational Exercises on Internet," Jiefangjun Bao (Liberation Army Daily) (Internet version), 10 July 2000 as translated and downloaded from the FBIS Web site on 10 July 2000.

[94] Yang Quansheng, Zhang Shusong, and Wang Yongqing, "Guangzhou Military Region Regiment Steps Up Capability to Fight Information Warfare," Jiefangjun Bao (Liberation Army Daily) (Internet version), 31 July 2000, p. 2 as translated and downloaded from the FBIS Web site on 31 July 2000.

[95] Ma Xiaochun and Xu Zhuangzhi, "Further Reinforcement Noted in Ability of Chinese Army to Win Future War," Xinhua Hong Kong Service, 16 October 2000 as translated and downloaded from the FBIS Web site on 16 October 2000.

new technologies, weapons, and methods of operation. In all, fifty-six research achievements were reported, focusing on resolving major issues faced in a modern war, such as combined operations, jamming, and so on. Each exercise is important since exercises explain the transition from theory to practice.

Chinese Perceptions of the IW Battle for Kosovo

The Chinese military also learned many IW-related lessons by observing coalition actions against Kosovo in 1999. China Military Science, in numbers 2, 3 and 4 of 1999, dedicated fifteen articles to the fight for Kosovo.

Chinese IW specialist Wang Baocun offered the best analysis of how both the Serbian Armed Forces and NATO used IW during the battle for Kosovo. Defining IW as "a military struggle in the information arena for the power to create information," he discussed NATO's offensive IW and Serbian defensive IW.[96]

NATO used IW in the preconflict stage, according to Wang, through extensive reconnaissance and monitoring of the potential conflict area. This included the use of military satellites, reconnaissance, and electronic monitoring. NATO began the next phase of the operation, the strike stage, by "beheading" the Yugoslav army's command system through a series of strikes. NATO then used IW superiority in the air (Serbian MiG-29's did not have advanced electronic-information systems to safeguard them) and waged an effective air war. At the same time, electronic-warfare capabilities focused on assessing battle damage. Thus from Wang's point of view, the NATO strike engagement package included electronic countermeasures, precision strikes, and damage assessment. Simultaneously a variety of psychological-warfare means were employed. Wang defined psychological warfare as "offensive warfare" aimed at changing the mental state of the enemy army and people. This included both defensive and offensive measures. Defensively, NATO first intensified the protection of its own information. In an offensive action, NATO prevented third parties from providing intelligence information to the Federal Republic of Yugoslavia (FRY). The latter included the creation of a NATO information blockade that prevented the Yugoslav army and people from obtaining key information.[97]

Active, protective measures taken by NATO were well advised and paid dividends. The Chinese Liberation Army Daily disclosed on 27 July 1999 that a "network battle" was fought between Chinese and US hackers following the 8 May bombing of the Chinese embassy. US hackers, according to the report, aimed their counterattack at the following Web sites:

Xin Lang Wang or Sina—http://home.sina.com.cn
Zhongwen Re Xun or Yesite—http://www.yesite.com
Shanghai Wang Sheng or Shanghai Web Boom (no http listed)

---

[96] Wang Baocun, "Information Warfare in the Kosovo Conflict," Jiefangjun Bao (Liberation Army Daily), 25 May 1999, p. 6 as translated and downloaded from the FBIS Web site on 23 June 1999.
[97] Ibid.

The Chinese initiated the short cyber war by altering the home page of the US Embassy in Beijing, writing on it "down with the Barbarians." The Chinese also reported that they caused a blackout at a few US political and military Web sites and some three hundred civilian Web sites. The methodology for performing these hacks, according to the PLA Daily article, was the mobilization of thousands and thousands of net users to issue a ping command to certain Web sites at the same time. This caused servers to overload and paralyzed these Web sites. In addition, thousands and thousands of e-mails were sent daily that blocked mail servers. Viruses were sent via e-mail, and attacks were launched with "hacker tools" hidden in certain programs. The PLA Daily article called for developing a computer network warfare capability, training a large number of network fighters in PLA academies, strengthening network defenses in China, and absorbing a number of civilian computer masters to take part in future network wars.[98]

Wang had high praise for the IW countermeasures utilized by Serb forces against NATO air attacks, especially the military deception of IW. The primary countermeasure was to use concealment to preserve Serb military strength. They did this by hiding planes in caves and along ring roads and highways; hiding armored vehicles in forests, near buildings in cities, and in mountains; allowing the army to disperse in cities and villages, mingling with the Albanians; and moving command and control organizations underground. They also used technical means to avoid enemy reconnaissance. These measures included not switching on air defense radar, calculating when military satellites would go over, putting greenery on armored vehicles or placing them next to heat sources, displaying corrugated iron and other radar "bait" to attract missiles and planes ("conceal the genuine and display the fake"), and taking advantage of weak points (such as the fact that surveillance cannot pierce smoke and clouds). Finally, like China, the Serbs used the Internet to fight NATO. They set up a number of sites on the worldwide web to describe how NATO was carrying out its air strikes, and they tried to overload NATO systems with excessive numbers of e-mail.[99]

A Chinese analyst noted that as the earth shrinks in virtual size via the use of information technology (telecommunications, the Internet, etc.), the size of the battlefield is actually growing. This includes, of course, all of the key nodes making up our virtual networks. The Chinese call attacks on key nodes "acupuncture war," where key points on the network become targets. Net points are of crucial importance to the survivability of a network. According to Metcalfe's Law "the value of a network is the square of the number of net points." So by destroying net points, one gets twice the results with half the effort in geometric terms. In addition to net point warfare, the Serbs learned valuable lessons from what the Chinese termed the "three anti's and one resistance." The three anti's included antireconnaissance, anti-interference, and anti-invisibility; and resistance meant working against destruction. The Chinese armed forces also noted that militaries must change from organizing according to weapon systems to organizing according to

---

[98] "Military Forum" page, Jiefangjun Bao (Liberation Army Daily), 27 July 1999, report obtained via e-mail from Mr. William Belk, 1 June 2000.
[99] Wang, "Information Warfare in the Kosovo Conflict."

information systems. The Chinese military must become flexible, more like "building blocks" that can be quickly restructured and reorganized.[100]

One article suggested that the Kosovo conflict was an example of the US' application of asymmetrical warfare. The latter was defined as "war between forces of different types, such as air force to navy, air force to army, navy to army, or army to air force." The key to asymmetrical warfare is to bring respective service advantages into full play, to pit the superior against the inferior, and to avoid strengths while attacking weaknesses. Interestingly, the author quoted Mao Zedong at this point, who suggested that many armies were against going head-to-head with other armies. As a counter, Mao believed that "we are not like Sung Hsiang-kung, not being so stupidly humane, just and virtuous." This belief certainly puts a different slant on asymmetry, sounding more like the book by two PLA colonels, Qiao Liang and Wang Xiangsui, entitled Unrestricted War! Asymmetrical war was further described as having smart-war characteristics, such as being grounded in technology, having information as its mainstay, developing in the direction of no-contact warfare, and making the battlefield more multidimensional. While this description of asymmetrical warfare is an over exaggeration of the concept, it still reflects how some Chinese interpreted it with regard to the fighting in Kosovo.[101]

Another article discussed NATO's information monopoly on the asymmetric battlefield. This meant that NATO could choose the forces, time, and space it wanted to apply combat power on the battlefield. This allowed it to control a larger battlefield radius than the other side. The understanding here is that one side's antenna or feelers can reach out farther than the other side's, enabling it to engage in no-contact or "beyond-defense" warfare. This ability offered absolute control of the situation. As a counter, the Chinese recommended developing anti-information, anti-air, and antibattlefield monopolies. The article suggested that in order to overcome these monopolies, China must "change our ideas, creating new battlefields such as the special operations battlefield, enemy-rear battlefield, and psychological-warfare battlefield." Some of these preparations must be done in a war's initial or preparation stage to ensure that no chance to strike is lost. Mao Zedong's statement about not practicing "any idiotic humanity" was then repeated by the author.[102]

Simple preparations helped to thwart or at least complicate some NATO IW missions. These preparations included, according to one source, a French officer from the Kosovo Organization for Security and Cooperation in Europe who gave the Serbian armed forces part of NATO's attack plan. It also included sending Serbian military experts (usually air defense personnel) to Iraq to learn how to fight against NATO and US planes (familiarity with radar signatures, flight patterns, etc.) and to conduct drills and

---

[100] Su Size, "Kosovo War and New Military Theory," Jiefangjun Bao (Liberation Army Daily), 1 June 1996, as translated and downloaded from the FBIS Web site on 1 July 1999.

[101] Jia Weidong, "Asymmetrical War and Smart War—The Developing Trends of Future War from a Kosovo Perspective," Jiefangjun Bao (Liberation Army Daily), 17 April 1999, p. 6 as translated and downloaded from the FBIS Web site on 10 May 1999.

[102] Zhu Xiaoning, "A Monopoly on the Asymmetrical Battlefield," Jiefangjun Bao (Liberation Army Daily), 23 November 1999, p. 6 as translated and downloaded from the FBIS Web site on 26 December 1999.

rehearsals that taught how to intercept cruise missiles.[103] Serb military personnel also learned how to camouflage key positions and equipment and how to build false targets (substitute telephone poles for main turrets in burnt-out armored vehicles, simulate communications on command and control nets, build fake bridges, etc.) that caused NATO to waste assets on the wrong targets.

An interesting training article with a Kosovo IW twist also appeared in the Chinese press. The article was a summary of the first, all-army collective training session for division and brigade chiefs of staff. Conducted by the Communications Command Academy, the instructors used the war in Kosovo as a frame of reference. The conference was held on 13 July 1999 shortly after the end of the fighting. One officer, Liu Xinsheng, noted that there were really four steps to NATO's combat performance. First, NATO used information reconnaissance operations to acquire precise intelligence information on strike targets. Second, NATO used hard weapons to destroy or paralyze command and control systems and air defense systems of the Yugoslav armed forces. Third, NATO used precision combat led by electronic warfare to attack military, economic, transportation, energy, public opinion, and other targets. Finally, NATO carried out damage assessments using airborne and ground photography and observations to determine the next bombing targets and make corrections. Information operations permeated these processes, such as NATO carrying out information blockades.[104]

The conference concluded that the Yugoslav armed forces hid their equipment well and used traditional tactics to counter NATO's high-tech reconnaissance missions. To deal with precision weapons, the Chinese stated that the Serbs divided the whole into parts, combining action with waiting and actively constructing a ground battlefield in which they moved to avoid destruction. They also studied the performance characteristics of Tomahawk cruise missiles to look for performance vulnerabilities. Tactics included:

- **Avoiding strikes**: By not turning on air defense radars, they kept NATO planes from finding their targets.
- **Hooking the fish**: They used folded corrugated steel or other materials as a decoy for radar, thus misleading the attacking missiles and aircraft.
- **Hide and seek**: They took advantage of the blind zones and dead angles in the operational orbits and dead space of NATO reconnaissance satellites.
- **Relay intercept**: They mixed the deployment of radars with different modalities and used the cross-deployment of weapons with different ranges to lay ambushes along the attack routes, switching on radar suddenly, performing intercept by firepower at different levels, and concentrating the fire of the weapons. This tactic was based on the mixed formations of NATO weaponry and their multi-echelon attacks.[105]

---

[103] Xinhua Hong Kong Service, 0527 GMT 24 May 1999 as translated and downloaded from the FBIS Web site on 26 May 1999.
[104] Sun, Yang, Zhang.
[105] Ibid.

Finally, the conflict over Kosovo convinced the PLA that it must use short-term solutions while modernizing. The goal of catching up with America in IW in the next two decades is not one filled with optimism, especially after watching the advanced performance of NATO weaponry. But there is a serious will to accomplish this goal, especially since building an information economy and a PLA IW capability go hand-in-hand. IW is not just simulations and precision weapons, but also hacking, electronic jamming and paralyzing, and conducting disinformation campaigns. A subgoal is to "wreak havoc on opponents' digital archives." The battle over Kosovo, from a Chinese point of view, actually helped to speed up PLA modernization by enhancing the move from mechanized forces to informationized forces.

Thus, the 1995-2000 period represented five years of learning and advancement for the Chinese military. The PLA learned by watching coalition actions in the Gulf War in 1991 and by watching the war over Kosovo in 1999. Not only was theory advanced, but exercises were held and new training methods presented. Chapter Two takes a closer look at the writings of Dr. Shen Weiguang, who is one of the primary Chinese IW theorists of this period. His analysis is important because it focuses on control as the most important aspect of IW and not strictly on information superiority or dominance as the US does.

CHAPTER TWO: THE THIRD WORLD WAR—TOTAL INFORMATION WAR
THE VIEWS OF CHINESE IW SPECIALIST SHEN WEIGUANG

Introduction

You were introduced to many IW authors in Chapter One. The purpose of this chapter is to highlight the IW theories of one of those authors, Dr. Shen Weiguang, who many consider the father of Chinese IW. He proposed the Chinese IW concept as early as 1985 and has since written several books on the subject. The focus of this chapter is his book World War, the Third World War—Total Information War.[106] Dr. Shen is also working on two other books that are probably published by now. They are The Mass Media and War and The Ideal War. Additionally, Shen has published twenty-three treatises since 1990. He is an innovative thinker who understands the many facets of IW and explains them with academic rigor. He is reportedly working for the State Council's Office of Structural Reform.

Shen has been especially active in defining IW and exposing its essence. As noted in Chapter One, in 1996 he offered a definition of IW that was one of the first from a Chinese perspective. He stated that IW is a war in which both sides strive to hold the battlefield initiative by controlling the flow of information and intelligence. This initial definition did not address information superiority or information operations—just control.[107] He listed the main tasks of IW as disrupting the enemy's cognitive system and its trust system.[108] This statement stands in stark opposition to the US predilection to focus predominantly on dominance and superiority of technological systems, often at the expense of cognitive systems.

In 1999 when Chinese analysts again returned to a serious debate over IW issues, Shen defined IW more broadly as involving two sides in pitched battle against one another in the political, economic, cultural, scientific, social, and technological spheres. The fight was for information space and resources. He also defined IW narrowly as the confrontation of warring parties in the field of information. The essence of IW, Shen wrote, is to attain the objective of "forcing enemy troops to surrender without a fight" through the use of information superiority.[109] This definition stressed superiority instead of control as was proposed in his 1996 definition of IW. However, in his work under

---

[106] Shen Weiguang, Excerpt from 'World War, The Third World War—Total Information Warfare,' Beijing: Xinhua Publishing House, January 2000, pp. 1-31, 213-331, 379-385 as translated and downloaded from the FBIS Web site on 17 May 2000. These excerpts serve as the basis for this chapter, and are not further footnoted.

[107] Shen Weiguang, [no title provided], Zhongguo Guofang Keji X, September-December 1996, Number 5/6, pp. 87-89 as translated and reported in FBIS-CHI-98-029, insert date 30 January 1998.

[108] Ibid.

[109] Shen Weiguang, "Checking Information Warfare-Epoch Mission of Intellectual Military," Jiefangjun Bao (Liberation Army Daily), 2 February 1999, p. 6 as translated and downloaded from the FBIS Web site on 17 February 1999.

consideration in this chapter, published in the same year, there was a greater focus on control than superiority.

Discussion of the Book: World War, the Third World War—Total Information War

The Foreign Broadcast Information Service (FBIS) translated excerpts from Shen's book <u>World War, the Third World War—Total Information War</u> which explored the evolving landscape of Chinese IW. It primarily focused on the period from 1997-2000, but it also included two presentations he made in 1989 and 1990. Paraphrased portions from the FBIS translations are provided in this chapter.

The distinguishing feature of Shen's IW discussion was his focus on the term "control" as opposed to the Western emphasis on information superiority. Shen noted that the purpose of IW is control [kong zhi], not bloodshed. Information control is the doorway to an opportunity to dominate the world, and the objective of IW is to capture the power to control information and the opponent's information and knowledge systems. Further, Shen stated that the objective of fighting has changed from destroying the enemy and preserving oneself to controlling the enemy and protecting oneself. Warfare will manifest itself as some form of control and as a search for a point of equilibrium of interests.

Shen defined IW in several ways in the book:

- Struggles in which two sides use the tools of information technology to obtain, control, and use information
- War aimed at capturing information space and seizing information resources
- The confrontation between two opposing groups in the information area in the course of an armed conflict
- People's War under high-tech conditions.

Other issues discussed in the book include themes as diverse as information deterrence, types of information weapons (a term the US does not define), Richard Nixon's books, and the use of thirty-six measures to disrupt the Internet. The book also includes Shen's description of:

- Specific Chinese IW objectives
- The purpose and advantages of using IW
- Elements, forms, objectives, and goals of IW
- The true significance of IW
- Application of IW principles to a People's War
- The purpose of information protection forces
- A new national strategy based on the requirements of the information age
- A recommended overhaul of the national defense and security structure of China

- A series of terms (soft military science, differential principle, etc.) that differ from Western terms.

Shen also discussed other interesting facets of Chinese military life and makes some bold suggestions to the leadership. He recommended changing the current system of seven military regions to three strategic command directions (more like the Russian "theater of military action" concept) and levying a tax on young people who do not take part in military service.

Finally, Shen identified Chinese sensitivities over "information territory" and "information borders" years before the collision of a US EP-3 surveillance and reconnaissance plane and a Chinese jet brought these terms to the world's attention. He noted in the book:

> The boundaries of "information territory" and the security of "information borders" determine the rise and fall of a nation and a country. All countries in the world are scrambling to expand their "information territories" and protect their invisible "information borders." A fierce battle to capture an edge in information territory is under way at this moment.

Interestingly, Shen took part in an exclusive interview with Guangzhou Ribao (daily newspaper of the Guangzhou city CPC committee) shortly after the EP-3 incident. He reportedly said that the US plane's collision with a Chinese military plane in China's territorial airspace has exposed the US government's consistent hegemonic thinking.[110] He was the first of a limited number of IW experts who commented on the affair.

FBIS translated excerpts of World War, the Third World War—Total Information War. The translation included seven chapters of the book plus it's preface and postscript. The preface was dated 20 November 1999. Chapter 1 is a speech delivered at the Lanzhou Military Region in April 1998. Chapter 2 is a speech delivered at China's National Defense University in Beijing in June 1998, and Chapter 3 is a lecture at China's Academy of Military Science in Beijing (no date provided). Chapter 4 is a speech delivered at the Information War Forum of the 19th Ars Electronica Festival at Linz, Austria, in September 1998. Chapters 5, 6, and 7 have dates of 1990, 1989, and December 1997, respectively, but no place or forum noted (speech, article, etc.). The postscript is dated 20 December 1999 from Hangzhou so there is apparently a one-month lag between the writing of the preface and postscript.

For this book the author has paraphrased selected portions of the FBIS translations. In the selection of excerpts from Shen's book that follows, it is important to keep in mind that the book represents the evolution of his ideas over the last decade. The author has **bolded** words or phrases in order to focus the reader's attention on important ideas and concepts. This allows the reader to speed read through the chapter for important concepts if desired. Additionally the author has added an introductory line(s) in *italics*

---

[110] Cheng, Feng, "Aircraft Collision Exposes US Naked Hegemonism," Guangzhou Ribao, 2 April 2001, as downloaded from the FBIS Web site on 2 April 2001.

describing the date and place (if available) of the speech. There are no footnotes for quotes since FBIS translations do not paginate in accordance with the pages in the actual article. Brackets [ ] indicate comments added by the author to further explain portions of the text.[111]

Dr. Shen's writings represent one influential voice among many in the Chinese debate over IW theory and practice. Shen's works are read by Chinese theorists and are considered very persuasive in the Chinese IW community. When Shen speaks, Westerners should also carefully consider what he has to say.

Paraphrased Translations from World War, the Third World War—Total Information War

Preface

Dr. Shen wrote the preface to the book on 20 November 1999. No further information about the preface is available.

In the preface, Shen notes that IW will be the leading form of war in the twenty-first century. This is because information, along with materials and energy, is one of mankind's three most valuable resources. Shen foresees the **control** of an information society as the doorway to the opportunity to dominate the world. This will be accomplished by the possession of information resources, the capture of information space, the expansion of information's frontier, and winning the battle for a foothold in an information society. The **main IW battlefield** will be intangible, information space, and this will cause a change in the state of war. The effect of this change will include the softening of strategic objectives, the development of information deterrence as a new means of deterrence [Shen believes that computer crime may exceed military attacks], the determination of military actions by the possession of information, the rising status of special forces, and the use of civilians on the battlefield. The **principal military objective** will be the disruption of the enemy's decision-making process. Every computer chip is a potential weapon; every computer may become an effective fighting platform; every citizen may develop a war plan and use the Internet to launch a special war. The **true significance of IW** lies in attacking man's thinking and morale.

Shen **broadly defines IW.** He notes:

IW is war between opposing military groups as well as political, economic, cultural, scientific, and technological groups and other groups from all sectors in society as they occupy information space and contest for information resources. Essentially it refers to action aimed at achieving a country's macro-strategic objectives through the use of information.

---

[111] Footnotes referencing items from the book are not used because the only reference is the English translation that does not correspond to the actual Chinese text.

The most important targets are computer network systems connecting a country's political, economic, and military installations. Any place within the reach of the network system may become an IW battlefield where geographical boundaries are irrelevant.

Narrowly defined, Shen looks at IW as: "The confrontation between two sides in the information arena in the course of an armed conflict, the purpose being to capture the power to **control** information." [Shen's focus on **control** is constant throughout his series of lectures].

Another consistent focus is the requirement to contain IW especially in a strategic sense. Shen offers several recommendations. First, he recommends drawing up a set of IW rules of engagement [a future arms control issue?] for two sides to comply with in case of conflict. Second, he recommends developing a strategy to prevent IW. On the other hand, Shen notes that China must have IW capabilities in order to prevent IW just as it needed nuclear weapons to prevent nuclear war. Shen notes that Russia's impotence over NATO actions in Kosovo demonstrated that nuclear weapons are not a universal bargaining chip and that Russia, too, must possess IW capabilities. IW alone cannot replace military power although it offers many advantages. It is cheap, not restricted to particular formats, and has no age or numerical restrictions on who can participate. IW capabilities must be backed up by military power.

Shen specifically highlights the psychological aspect of IW, enumerating the goals and purposes behind the West's "**peaceful evolution strategy**" which he states works better than a global containment strategy. He sees a peaceful evolution strategy as a more effective, modern day version of a global containment strategy. Shen defines **peaceful evolution** as a strategy of deception that lowers public vigilance, an inflammatory form of psychological war. He credits former US President Richard Nixon with eloquently describing this concept in two books, 1999: Victory Without War, and The Real War. In the first book Shen highlights Nixon's phrase that "World War III began well before World War II ended," and in the second book, he highlights Nixon's statement that "there is a gray area between peace and war, and the struggle will be largely decided in that area." Shen believes the "gray" area to be IW, and that here is where the Third World War—total IW—will be fought. He defines **all-out IW** as a global confrontation in which the two opposing sides compete for and seize information space and information resources. One of the forms of total IW will be **information aggression**, defined as violating the information space of another country and plundering its information resources. A concrete example was one country disseminating the aggressor's thoughts and ideas to another country to influence the latter via the proliferation of mass media outlets. Shen noted that socialist countries worldwide must be on the defensive against this type of war while simultaneously pursuing a policy of offense-oriented defense.

Shen states that twenty-first century warfare in an information age is man-centered and seeks to destroy ideas, spirit, and thought. The **purpose of IW** is **control** [kong zhi], not bloodshed. The **foremost goal** is to attack the human spirit. The most effective tools are strategic competition, deterrence theory, public-opinion war, potential confrontation, and psychological war.

Shen implies that the information age has introduced a reinterpretation of Clausewitz's dictum that war is a continuation of politics by other means. His reinterpretation is based on the fact that war was the politician's tool, and the politician controlled information such that the people did not know what was really going on. Now, information is shared, and the masses should run the show since war is society's business. The networking of societies encourages the role of society and diminishes the role of the armed forces. IW also encourages what Shen terms "ideal war" or victory without war.

IW is more frequently fought for economic interests than political interests today, and it is difficult to tell what a military action is and what social behavior is. In this sense, new types of war may have emerged. These potentially include **intellectual war**, where the purpose is to limit war to within the thinking stage; **simulated war**, where technology simulates reality and information deterrence tools to check an opponent's intent (making the purpose of war "controlling the enemy and preserving oneself" through Internet confrontations and online military exercises); **warning war**, where the purpose is to instill fear in the opponent or any potential enemy and serve as a warning (Kosovo was a warning to those observing NATO actions); **war as a contest**, where the purpose is to stage contests in overall national strength and combat capability and engage in military confrontation at regular or irregular intervals (there has never been a war as contest, but there are many joint exhibitions of military might, according to Shen); and **war among leaders**, where the purpose is to win the intellectual battle. Shen believes an ideal form of war now exists which is based on developments in science and technology, social progress and the growing inclination toward peace among mankind. Shen does not, however, disqualify the destructiveness of war, even under IW conditions.

Chapter One

The Lanzhou Military Region asked Dr. Shen in April 1998 to address the evolution and current status of IW theoretical research and the concept and content of IW both in China and abroad. Shen divided his response into three parts: challenge, objective and countermeasure (underlined in the section below). This chapter was called "Welcome the Great Challenge of the New Military Revolution of the Modern World: Achieve the Historic Leap from Mechanized War to IW." It is the most interesting and detailed chapter in the book.

Challenge: Placing IW against the Backdrop of the RMA.
One cannot ignore the revolution in military affairs (RMA). For example, speaking of the Russians, Shen noted how precision-guided weapons combine real-time surveillance with command and control into one unit. Shen considered the US definition of the RMA as representative of "three news and two changes." The "news" were represented by combining new weapons systems with new military theories and new organizational structures. The "two changes" were the characteristics of war and the methods of fighting a war. In China the substance, content, significance, characteristics, and historical development of the military revolution are studied. In addition, former

Chairman Jiang Zemin stressed a strategic policy for the Chinese military that put forward a specific strategic objective calling for "two fundamental changes" in which during military preparation for action the focus would shift from winning a limited war under regular conditions to winning a limited war under high-tech conditions; and in military buildup, the focus would shift from the quantitative model to the qualitative model, from the manpower-intensive model to the science and technology-intensive model. Shen also explored the development of IW theory in the US from the early 1980s to March 1996, noting that digitalized units in the US Army improved their raid-response capability and combat effectiveness threefold.

In discussing the development of IW in China, Shen began by pointing out his own seminal work on IW in 1985 and his 1990 book Information War. He then noted the work of Qian Xuesen, ascribing to him the idea of IW under conditions of nuclear deterrence. He also noted the work of Zhu Guangya who said that information and knowledge have unique attributes. Zhu stated that they spread globally, can be disseminated at the speed of light, have non-linear effects, are inexhaustible, and can be shared by many people. Information can **control** and manipulate material and energy, thus boosting combat effectiveness and reducing the need for other types of inputs. Information and knowledge are a multiplier of power since:

> In the past military power was calculated simply by adding up the number of armored divisions, aircraft, and aircraft carriers. Now we must figure in some intangible forces as well, such as computing capability, communications capability and reliability, and real-time surveillance ability. Practice proves that "an ounce of silicon in the computer may be more potent than a ton of radium."

Objective: Moving from Mechanized to Information War.
Shen noted that there is no universal definition of IW and showed this by offering the diverse views of US specialists. He drew on the work of Martin Libicki, Alan Campen, the C3I office in the Pentagon, the US Air Force's three definitions of IW, the Navy definition, the 1995 National Defense Report, and a host of other sources.

Shen states that most definitions have a few things in common, namely that they all want to seize an information advantage, that they stress both offensive and defensive aspects, and that they focus on the destruction of information systems and facilities or the circulators of information. Shen then **defines IW** from this discussion as a struggle in which two sides use the tools of information technology to obtain, **control**, and use information.

Shen ascribes the confusion in the US over terminology to a failure to differentiate among four terms: war in the information age, information warfare, information war, and information fighting. He personally uses the concepts of information-based warfare and IW most often. Information-based warfare includes IW both on and off the battlefield. The former refers to troops engaging in battle in the information area on the battlefield, the **control** and **countercontrol** of military information, and the destruction and counterdestruction of military information. The latter refers to the protection of and attack on the information infrastructure and the ability to obtain information and process information in order to achieve some given political objective.

Shen states that IW is composed of six elements: obtaining information, using information, protecting information, utilizing information, denying information, and managing information. Using information means analyzing and verifying information. Utilizing information means making full use of one's information, information systems, and the enemy's information and information systems to accomplish military objectives.

Shen lists several IW characteristics. First is the fact that both offensive and defensive war is waged in the electromagnetic and psychological arenas. Second, the **objective of IW** is to capture and **control** information. **Control** allows for combat effectiveness to be utilized. Third, IW is waged through **information weapons** and information systems. This refers to weapons, equipment, and systems centered on information technology including information-based platforms. **Lethal information weapons** (information-based weapons) include precision-guided weapons, remote-sensing lethal weapons, electromagnetic pulse (EMP), biological, and nano- weapons. **Soft lethal information weapons** and systems include electronic, photoelectric, and acoustic jammers; computer viruses; and equipment for psychological warfare. These weapons and systems integrate the battlefield, making the battlefield more transparent and diversifying the avenues to victory as well as the means to achieve it. Fourth, the command, control, communication, computer, and information systems (Shen's C4I) confrontation is the **main content of IW.** Its **paramount objective** is to suppress, weaken, damage, and destroy the opponent's C4I. Fifth, IW is closer to real-time discovery, command, attack, mobilization, and assurance than other types of war. This increases combat space while lessening troop density and, perhaps, the duration of the fight. Finally, the **main objective of IW** is information damage by attacking, weakening, and interfering with enemy information systems so that information loses its integrity, authenticity, accuracy, usability, and timeliness. Forms of information damage include deceptive, obstructionist, isolationist, and contaminating and directional damage. The **essence of IW** is to use one's information edge. This means using information fully, accurately, and in a timely fashion, while denying the enemy these abilities [which sounds like the US definition of information superiority] to achieve the defeat of the enemy without fighting.

Shen lists four **levels of IW**: national IW, national defense IW, strategic IW, and tactical IW. He also lists **two "natures"** of IW: peacetime IW, which includes economic IW, cultural IW, reality-simulated war, psychological war, and Internet war; and wartime IW, which includes some peacetime elements. Shen noted that instead of shaping the battlefield, information is now starting to **control** the battlefield. Regarding psychological war, some Third World countries now consider the invasion of Western, especially American, culture as an IW attack on values.

IW departs from traditional war in several ways. First, the contest on the battlefield has moved from fire and blood to a contest in spirit, will, and intelligence on a silent battlefield. Shen states we have entered the era of "brain war." Second, there has been a move from hard attack to soft damage. The **objective of IW** is to **control** the opponent's information and knowledge systems, especially the thinking of military decision makers and commanders. **IW aims** to **control** the enemy and protect oneself. Third, and most important, the military is no longer the only armed group. Many weapons and equipment can be bought on the civilian market, and even nonlethal equipment is now developed by the civilian sector. It is civilian technology that enjoys an advantage in IW. Fighting is not confined to the battlefield but occurs all over society. IW is, to a certain extent, a **"People's War"** in another form. Fourth, IW stresses defense more than offense since even small and weak countries have access to information weapons and could attack unexpectedly. On the other hand, if enemy intent is clear, "attack in order to defend" may be more effective than defense alone. Fifth, traditional boundaries between government agencies are now blurred [since some boundaries occur in cyberspace]. Computer crime can be as damaging as a military attack. Boundaries among intelligence, defense, law enforcement, and other government agencies are now more meaningless. There is no front in IW. Sixth, IW is brain war. Information must be transformed from data (unprocessed information) to information (processed data) to knowledge (synthesized, analyzed, and evaluated information) to intelligence (understanding at a higher level after further synthesis). China needs advanced weapons both to wage war and to deter war.

> In the future countries of the world should formulate a set of rules for information war that would stipulate that IW is only a contest, that man's common interests, especially man himself, cannot be harmed…information technology will mercilessly tear up the foundation of industrial society and fashion an industrial structure, a way of life, and even an ideology for the information age.

<u>Countermeasures: Developing an Offensive and Defensive Strategy for China</u>.

War is more than the continuation of politics and more than the highest form of conflict. It is a way through which nonpolitical organizations, even individuals, further their interests and demonstrate their existence. War knows no boundaries. Enterprises, religious organizations, terrorist organizations, ethnic guerrillas, drug-trafficking rings, and other crime syndicates can all launch IW. The **objective** of fighting wars is changing from "destroy the enemy and preserve oneself" to "**control** the enemy and protect oneself." Strategically the **objective of war** in the information age is to destroy the enemy's will to launch a war or to wage a war by disrupting the enemy's decision-making process or paralyzing its power system. It is hard to say if wars are just or unjust today.

War will manifest itself as some form of **control** and a search for a point of equilibrium of interests. The **objective of IW is control**, not bloodshed. To affect **control** a variety of nonlethal wars have been developed. **Information deterrence**, the ability to wage IW and information support capability, will play a major role in war prevention. China needs a new war outlook and national strategy. Some of the elements of that new view include the following:

1. There is a new war view where the **objective of IW** is to destroy the enemy's political, economic, and military information infrastructures. Because of IW, war is not confined to the military field, but has spread to political, economic, social, cultural, and other arenas.
2. China must formulate a national information offensive and defensive strategy. It must adopt an offensive strategy in IW.
3. China must establish a national information security commission to strengthen centralized leadership over IW research, to oversee and assume total responsibility for the nation's information security, and to organize research on IW theories and on the technology and equipment of IW. Information security and IW is a systems engineering piece with no precedent. **China needs an information security and IW studies institute** at the highest level.
4. China must create a unified and open-research system on military theories that unites the battlefield and society; the military and the civilian. Electronics experts, computer experts, and information engineers may become the true heroes of the new battlefield and may have to fight a war in the office and at home. The military, society's academic institutes, and individuals must interact with and complement one another.
5. China must strive for breakthroughs in critical information technologies and develop them at home instead of relying on foreign systems as this would damage the information security of the country. China must also develop its own chip research, including encryption, analytical decryption, computer viruses, network attack, network security, interference, and counterinterference.
6. China must develop information-age deterrent forces. In order to stand up to other countries, China must develop measures to counter viruses, EMP, lasers, and photoelectric-wave weapons in order to neutralize and check Western powers' deterrence capabilities.
7. China must issue information security assessments, establish inspection standards, and accelerate the creation of an information security law-enforcement contingent. It must establish information security standards and rules of conduct. It must test, analyze, evaluate, and verify the security of key national information systems.
8. China must set up a national-level "information confrontation laboratory" to keep China from becoming too passive and capable of only reacting. The lab will allow China to take a proactive stance so that IW issues can be solved in peacetime.
9. China must reform its fragmented and independent intelligence organizations and establish a centralized comprehensive information intelligence system.

China also needs an overhaul of its traditional national defense and security structure. The creation of a new system would be suited to the needs of the information age. This new structure should include:

1. **An emphasis on information security**. Information security is the cornerstone of overall national security, and it must be elevated to the top. The political turmoil in China in 1989 was the result of China's information system being compromised and disrupted.

41

2. **Active participation in international security cooperation**. China must initiate official and unofficial security cooperation in all areas and at all levels with the international community while adhering strictly to principles. China must not isolate itself or be excluded by the international community.

3. **Adjustments to the thinking behind defense buildups**. The objective of defense buildup should be to establish the qualitative superiority of information technology, equipment, and systems. Regarding the scale of the defense buildup, China should reduce the "actual" and strengthen the "potential," while maintaining a standing army of 1.5-2 million men.

4. **Reinforcement of the "spiritual defense line."** Computers are being used to disseminate and export political views and values, even vilifying other counties. Some computers are used to create chaos by spreading false information aimed at confusing the public. China believes that the spirit of the nation and the people is the first thing the enemy will go after.

5. **Construction of an information frontier**. The space within the reach of a nation's or a political group's influence has become its **"information territory."** An information attack can penetrate the enemy's military, political, economic, and social spheres. Future strength depends on the expansion of a nation's "information territory" and the security of its "information borders."

6. **The establishment of an "information defense force."** The emergence of information borders makes it imperative that a corresponding "information defense force" be established. China needs technology-intensive specialized forces made up of scientists, information experts, policemen and soldiers well versed in IW to defend the security of the nation's information borders. This includes crackdowns on information criminal activities and the performance of emergency repairs caused by network incidents [which sounds like the US' computer emergency response teams (CERT)].

Another requirement is to reform the armed forces and create an information-based army with Chinese characteristics. This would entail:

1. **Reform the national defense system**. This requires strengthening the role and functions of the offices of the Central Military Commission (CMC) and beefing up the CMC's leadership over the coordination of the various headquarters.

2. **Reform the command system**. IW requires that command be highly efficient and that intermediate points in the transmission of information be minimized. The existing military regions should be changed into three-service joint battle zone commands. The group army should be eliminated, and the number of battle zone commands should be adjusted as appropriate depending on the strategic direction and mission. Training should be separated from the Joint Staff so that the latter can focus on commanding the entire army in wartime and organizing military exercises.

3. **Reform the high-level leadership management system**. Reform of the leadership system at central command, at the various arms of the services, and in the military regions is needed. An organization should be developed to take

charge of the training, development, administration, and political and logistical work for the various arms of the military.

4. **Reform the system of colleges and univer**sities. The military academies should be integrated into the nation's educational system so that the leadership can make plans in a centralized way for training qualified personnel. The military should establish an information academy or have the appropriate colleges or universities offer a new discipline in IW to train qualified personnel for future IW.

5. **Reform the logistical syste**m. There is a need for open-bidding, fixed-point procurement, and shared ownership.

6. **Reform the conscription system through a mixture of professionalization and compulsory conscription**. Military officers who are professionals should staff key, technology-intensive positions. The government may exempt people from the related fees during the period of study if they are willing to devote themselves to the vocation of national defense. A national defense tax should be levied on those young people who do not perform military service.

7. **Streamline agencies at all levels and eliminate unnecessary troops and organizations.**

8. **Eliminate obsolete weaponry and intensifying the development of information-based weaponry.** Much of the obsolete weaponry inherited from the mechanized era should be eliminated as soon as possible, and resources should be pooled to develop the weaponry required in the information age.

9. **Reform weaponry procurement practices**. Defense needs should be met through market-bidding and policy guidance. The armed forces must put a complete stop to their involvement in production and business.

10. **Establish a "launching fund" for military reform**. Set up a military reform fund to help further the deepening of military reform.

Chapter Two

In June 1988, Dr. Shen delivered a lecture on IW to the Chinese National Defense University. It was called "New Situation, New Challenges."

The strategic link in international relations is no longer the confrontation and arms race between the superpowers, but the quarrels and arguments between businessmen from different countries and the debate between nations over values. Information has power, and people are afraid of missing out on information. Today the masses can get information as fast as people at the upper echelons of power, and information can be shared among the masses. Simultaneously, someone can watch TV and go on the Internet. Time differences are reduced, and person-to-person relations are strengthened. War now seeks out information space and information resources instead of plundering wealth and land. The **main factor** in deciding who wins and who loses a war is no longer the possession of material resources and manpower but the possession of information. Many people think the Gulf War was won with US military technology and Russian military thinking. Today the US is preparing for IW. It has developed a theory of IW and IW strategy, developed an integrated C4ISR system, conducted secret research on offensive IW, studied defensive IW, and conducted simulated IW exercises.

China is also working on an IW strategy. For example, in the Shenyang Military region there was organized:

> military exercises in IW using live soldiers; it came up with more than 20 achievements, which were tested. On the computer, people have come up with 36 ways to disrupt the Internet and 36 ways to defend against such disruption. There are also proposals to create a social order for the future information world.

The **purpose of IW** is to capture an information advantage using both offensive and defensive actions. The **target of attack** in IW could be information systems and facilities, or it could be the circulation process of information. Accordingly, IW could be described as a struggle in which the two sides primarily use tools of information technology and equipment to obtain, **control**, and use information. There are two types of IW. They are strategic IW and tactical IW. The former refers to actions outside the physical battlefield, and its goal is to create a policy that establishes an atmosphere of conflict. Tactical IW is battlefield IW, namely command and **control** warfare and decision-making **control** warfare. Its goal is to use information as the main weapon to attack the enemy's knowledge and information systems to influence, alter, or end the resolve of decision makers. **Forms of IW** include psychological war, intelligence war, strategic competition, theoretical deterrence, potential confrontation, electronic war, firepower war intended to destroy information facilities, computer virus war, precision war, invisible war, and so on.

IW is a contest in human intelligence and wisdom. The **forces of IW**, such as advanced weapons used for deterrence purposes, are no longer entirely confined to the armed forces but are scattered among the scientists' laboratories and throughout all sectors of society. The true meaning of IW can be found when computers, networking, and the human brain are used jointly. **Control** over information determines the freedom of movement of an army as much as control over land, sea, air, and outer space. **Control** over information cannot be equated with technological superiority. The **main target of an IW attack** is to disrupt the enemy's decision-making process, and the **main objective of IW** is to attack the enemy's knowledge system and faith system. The **characteristics of IW** are precision and speed. The role of special units exemplifies an IW force's flexibility, efficiency and compactness. **IW is a People's War under high-tech conditions** executed through networks in society as well as through the military. The extensive mobilization and utilization of civilian forces assumes extra significance, and the overall cohesiveness of a nation becomes a source of war power. In **IW the goal is control** not bloodshed, and, as a result, a series of nonlethal weapons have appeared one after another in the wake of the rapid development of information technology.

War has become a way for nonpolitical organizations and even individuals to further their interests and demonstrate their existence. The ability to paralyze and **control** the enemy is replacing the ability to destroy and annihilate him. **Strategically the objective of war in the information age** is to destroy the enemy's will to launch a war or wage a war. Tactically, the aim is to paralyze the enemy's power system. The information age makes it impossible to identify many armed conflicts, military actions, and limited wars as either just or unjust based on their nature. Both the nature of war and methods of fighting have become diversified in the information age. Warfare will manifest itself as some form of **control** and the search for a point of equilibrium of interests, not the occupation of cities and the plundering of land. In IW war preparation and war execution blend into each other. Also, the ability to wage IW and obtain an information support capability will be a powerful new deterrence factor (which Shen calls "information deterrence") and will play a major role in preventing war.

Strategically the objective of IW is to destroy the enemy's political, economic, and military information infrastructures, and, perhaps, even the information infrastructure for all of society. This includes destroying and paralyzing the enemy's military, financial, telecommunications, electronic, and power systems, and computer networks. It includes conducting PSYWAR and strategic deception. Strategic IW never stops for a minute. Witness Radio Free Europe's never ending broadcasts. China must understand the nature of this covert and invisible attack, and it must understand and accept IW and cultivate a new view of war.

War has moved from hard attack to soft damage. The **objective of IW** is to **control** the opponent's information system and knowledge system, especially the thinking of military decision makers and commanders. At the same time a country must protect itself from the same. IW means system-to-system soft damage. Additionally, IW targets may be civilians. Weaponry can be bought and sold on the civilian market. IW is **People's War** in a true sense of the term since fighting is not confined to the battlefield. "Attack in order to defend" is more effective than defense alone in many cases since advance warning is impossible and the effectiveness of defense is hard to predict. Networks cloud the geographical boundaries between nations and regions, and it is hard to tell where the threat of IW comes from, who is under attack, and who should be held accountable. This elevates computer crime to a status on par with a traditional military attack. IT has made geographical distances meaningless since an IW battlefield is anywhere within reach of a computer network. There is no front in IW, and the number of strategic targets grows as society becomes more and more information-based. Finally IW is "brain war."

China must have new weapons in order to both wage war and to deter war. In IW the battlefield is invisible information space. War is no longer the highest form of struggle, and it does not express itself as a conflict between two opposing armed forces. The nation-state may no longer be the only instigator of war. In the networked world of the future every microchip becomes a potential weapon; every computer has the potential to be an effective fighting unit; and every ordinary citizen may write a computer program for waging war. What was new about the Gulf War was that information systems were attacked, and the information attack has given rise to a new way of fighting. Virus-infected microchips can be put in weapon systems; an arms manufacturer can be asked to write a virus into software; or a biological weapon can be embedded into the computer system of an enemy nation and then activated as needed. Thus, war preparation takes on another form. Preparation for a military invasion can include hiding self-destructing microchips in systems destined for export. War preparation and war execution coincide.

Broadly defined, IW includes propaganda war, the battle for public opinion, and social-psychological war. It is a battle to influence, **control**, and attack the other side's policy-making concepts and identification system. It is war fought in the ideological arena. The information age has made IW easier since communication channels between different classes and social groups have multiplied. Media globalization has reduced the influence of a single medium, a single frequency, a single publication, or a single technology that will break the monopoly that a regime exercised over information in the past. The line between national politics and international politics is also blurred as a silent transfer of power is taking place. This makes it easier for social groups and individuals to directly participate in political activities in their own country or in any given country. Countries have become economically interdependent as well. The higher the dependency on information, the greater the threat becomes. Culture is the glue for society and the foundation for social stability. It sets social norms and defines and shapes every social system. Cultural confusion will ultimately affect the security of a nation's social strata. Confusion can intensify in the transition to an information society.

Regardless, any war has its origin in the human brain. The basic combat units taking part in "brain war" are the human brain + external brain (think tank) + computer. If total IW is IW at its fullest, then "brain war" is IW at its smallest. Every IW is made up of countless brain wars of various sizes. **Future world war, total IW, begins with a "brain war."**

China must also defend its information border. The traditional concept of national borders has been challenged. Now a string of questions arises about preserving national "communications sovereignty" and "information sovereignty" and protecting national secrets. The Internet is a "New World" with no border and no treaties. The primary targets of attack in IW are the computer network systems that connect the enemy's political, economic, and military facilities and the entire society. An **information border** is an irregular and invisible line that delimits the information territory of a nation or political group. **Information territory** is not based on the traditional concepts of territory, air space, territorial waters, or even outer space, but on information space with political clout. An information territory is a natural product of the information age while an information border is the result of the evolution and development of the forms of war. Information adds a fifth dimension to war. Countries with advanced networking technology rely on networks to expand their "information territory" to many other countries and threaten the latter's "information sovereignty." Since the information movement is network-based, it in turn determines that competitive confrontation must be network-based. A **"network frontier" conflict** seeks to confuse, disrupt, threaten, and damage the other side by using networks, breaking into the opponent's networks, preventing network penetration, spreading threatening information on the network to deter aggression, and attacking and damaging the opponent's "network frontier" to create loopholes one can exploit.

If a country lacks combat effectiveness for a given dimension of the battlefield, it would in effect succumb on the border for that dimension or for all dimensions. The information-dimension requires China to build an information defense and build an information border. Figuring out where to draw the information border and how to do so to promote the dissemination and spread of positive useful information and prevent or reduce the dissemination of negative, useless, and even harmful information is the challenge. A successful information border will ensure national information security and the integrity of national information sovereignty. The creation of such concepts requires that "information protection forces" be created. The force must be technology-intensive and totally different from traditional forces. It should be composed of scientists, information experts, and soldiers proficient in IW. The force would secure the nation's information frontier, counter information invasions, and crack down on criminal activities. Such a task force would also implement IW, serving as a "crash unit" that would perform emergency repairs after an "information incident."

The **essence of IW** is that it targets the human heart with the weapon of information. It attacks the will of the nation, the morale of the troops, and the resolve of the commanders. The spirit of the nation as well as the spirit of the individual is a "window vulnerable to attack." IW requires that electronics experts, computer scientists, and information engineers become the true heroes of the new battlefield. China must change its personnel and old ways of thinking before it changes anything else. Generals must base their strategic and tactical thinking on technology. A major IW principle is the **differential principle**. This principle is applied when an information-based force goes to war against a non-information-based force. Usually the former will have the upper hand. China must stress the development of **soft military science**. It is a science that deals specifically with military theories, military strategies, military planning, and military management.

Chapter Three

The following lecture was delivered at the Chinese Academy of Military Science, but no date of the delivery of the speech was noted. It was called "Some Thoughts on IW."

IW is war aimed at capturing information space and seizing information resources. IW talk, however, is stuck at talking only about applications of information and technology in an armed conflict such as network attacks and hacking. What is the purpose of war? Is it destruction or **control**? More often than not, it is economic interests and not political interests that is the **purpose of war**. This is because the ties between the military field and other fields are closer than ever before. The only way to appreciate the significance of IW is to do so from the perspective of society and strategy. The **formation and development of IW went through three stages:**

1. **The mid-1980s to the outbreak of the Gulf War in 1991.** The first applications of information technology were not in the military field but in the economy and in daily life. What was new about the Gulf War was that the multinational forces went after the enemy's information systems with their information weapons. This was a different way of attacking than in the past.

2. **From the Gulf War to 1998**. The use of IW in the Gulf War caused enthusiasm everywhere for this new type of war. The US used "information deterrence" to keep from fighting in Haiti and achieved their objective by "crushing the enemy without fighting." As a result information science secured its place as an important multidisciplinary science. General Fu Quanyou demanded the development of ways that inferior equipment could defeat superior equipment, and he wanted to develop a strategic technology of **People's War**. The Communications and Command College of the PLA introduced two new fields of study—IW command and control science, and IW featuring live soldiers. Thirty-six ways were developed to disrupt the network and thirty-six ways to protect against such disruption. The Chinese Academy of Social Sciences set up the Information Security Technology and Engineering Center and the National Laboratory for Information Security. Professional magazines, such as <u>IW Forum</u>, were developed. Some units created information networks linked to the information superhighway's combat-simulation models and elementary combat laboratories. Some private organizations founded IW research institutes since people were worried that the Internet might touch off a world war.

3. **The next stage began in 1998**. As the world continues to network, the destructiveness of IW will reveal itself in full force. Destruction of the network might paralyze the whole world in an instant. IW includes **strategic competition, the battle for public opinion, and theoretical deterrence** (the first could represent computer network attack and computer network defense [CNA/CND] and the Internet, the second PSYOP and IO, and the third the informationization of weaponry). As society becomes more information-based, the number of strategic targets vulnerable to strategic attack will increase. Therefore, China must contain IW, not develop it. **A set of information rules** to be honored by both sides should be developed. IW should not be allowed to threaten mankind as some sort of contest. The world as a whole needs an "international IW forum" to step up exchanges and cooperation to contain or limit IW in the interest of world peace.

Deterrence is inherently a new **form** of IW. The top brass must decide if a **special IW service** is needed. IW offers a number of advantages. It can take a variety of forms, is inexpensive, uses a number of tools to score a victory, is more acceptable to the public, and has no age, sex, or numerical restrictions on the participants. The **key** is to infuse technical matters with the thinking of a strategist. Strategically speaking, IW knows no boundaries and has no restrictions on distance. The **objective of fighting** is changing from destroying the enemy to **controlling** the enemy. War will manifest itself as the quest for some form of **control**. To effect **control**, and as a corollary to the rapid development of information technology, a variety of nonlethal weapons have appeared in succession. The **strategic objective of war** is to destroy the enemy's will to launch a war or wage a war. China must develop an **IW containment strategy** without delay. Forces can be balanced only through mutual checks. Information deterrence can be buttressed if someone has the ability to wage IW and has an information support capability. It can play a role in war prevention and war escalation. [Shen also described his new war view and idea of a new national strategy in this speech at the Academy of Military Sciences, as he did at Lanzhou Military Region in April 1998.]

Chapter Four

This is a lecture delivered by Dr. Shen at the Information War forum at the 19th Ars Electronica Festival, Linz, Austria on 12 September 1998. It is entitled "Fight to Stop Military Wars."

Most definitions of IW agree that the **purpose of IW** is to seize an information advantage, that IW includes both offensive and defensive actions, and that IW targets information systems and facilities or the circulation processes of information. IW can be **defined** as a struggle in which the two sides rely mainly on tools of information technology to obtain, control, and use information. **Broadly defined, IW** refers to a war in which opposing military (or political, economic, etc.) groups vie to capture information space and information resources. Information is mainly used to achieve larger national strategic objectives. **Narrowly defined, IW** refers to the confrontation between two warring parties in the information field. The **essence of IW** is to use one's information edge to crush the enemy without fighting. Having an **information edge** is one of the main things that will determine who wins and who loses. It is a multiplier of power. **Information superiority** means one has the ability to freely utilize information while the enemy does not have such ability. An army's freedom of movement is determined by its **control** over information. **Control** over information does not mean technological superiority. New tactics determine **control** as well as the independent creativity of the commanders in the field. The **main objective of attack in IW** is to disrupt the enemy's decision-making process and his knowledge and information systems. Speed and precision are the **characteristics of IW**. Over-the-horizon precision assault will be the basic application of firepower. Point-directed structural damage will replace traditional fighting. The traditional pagoda-type of command systems will become more flat or level. **IW is People's War under high-tech conditions**. The most crucial element is not technology but human decision-making behavior.

Shen believes that information technologies have highlighted command as an art, and they will subsequently offer more room for strategic applications. In addition, the front and rear type of forces may change places. In IW the high-tech troops may be private sector professionals that fight first while the armed forces are used in a deterrent back-up role. The **primary targets** of attack in IW are human thoughts, especially those of policy-makers. **First targets** would be computer networks connecting the enemy's political, economic, and military installations and society. Ordinary people may be targets as well. Thus, in a real sense, IW is a **People's War**. Any individual or social organization armed with communications technology and equipped with a computer and a telephone line with access to a computer network can attack information systems, thus launching a **special war** through the network.

So far we have only seen the civilized side of IW. China should be alert for a surprise attack coming from cyberspace. Political security has been threatened like never before. This has made politics more transparent and raised the level of political democratization. It will also make political security more vulnerable. The political regime's monopoly on information will be broken due to increasing communication channels between different classes and countries. This creates opportunities for social groups and individuals to participate directly in the political activities in their own countries. A silent transfer of power is taking place. Culture sets social norms and defines and shapes every social system. Cultural confusion ultimately will affect social security. Thus, reports of EMP and virus devices hope to paralyze an economy and upset society.

Chapter Five

The following is a 1990 speech, topic and place not noted. It is titled "Nineteen Nineties: Era of IW."

To be an effective deterrent a theory must be original, advanced, timely, and exclusive. Unrealized theories, for example, have no deterrent value because they have lost their timeliness. Potential of many types can be converted into a **deterrent information capability** that can stop aggression. This potential must be in abundance, and it must be advanced to truly represent a deterrent. The development of psychological, science, and technology and other forces can form such an effective **deterrent** and force an opponent to submit.

Psychological war is war that belongs in the realm of invisible IW. There is strategic PSYWAR, which takes place in peacetime and wartime. And there is tactical PSYWAR, which takes place mainly in the war zone. The West has sixty radio stations devoted to PSYWAR, and they broadcast 450 hours of programming each day.

In terms of time and space, there are two types of wars. One is the violent type that takes place on the battlefield. It is temporary in duration and limited in scale. The other type is **deterrent war** that occurs outside the battlefield. It takes up all the space and time not taken up by its violent counterpart, or may include it. In a **deterrent war**, opposing sides convert their power into information and deterrence that in turn gives rise to IW in a number of areas. Efforts are aimed at stopping the opponent's belligerent behavior and strategy. Deterrence war has been in existence and has never waned since the start of history. IW is inherently deterrent war. IW and deterrence are like two wheels on an axle as neither could do without the other. **Broadly defined, IW** refers to a war between opposing military groups as they vie for space and compete for information resources. **Narrowly defined, IW** refers to the confrontation between the two opposing sides in the information area in the course of an armed conflict. **Information space** refers to the invisible space resulting from the complex development of information networking and information technologies. IW is thus invisible war. It consists of new strategies or invisible methods of confrontation that ignite one invisible IW after another. **IW characteristics** include: in terms of **format**, IW can be either visible or invisible; in terms of **duration**, IW is long-termed or phased; in terms of **scale**, it is indefinite or finite; and in terms of **content**, it is expansionary or compressible. Science and technology developments have resulted in a qualitative change in mankind's understanding of information. War is freeing itself from the straitjacket of traditional theories and leaving the confines of lower-levels for a higher-level and more perilous realm. This may lead to **information factories, information frontiers, information alliances, and information military police**. Clearly, from the 1990s into the twenty-first century, **IW** (deterrence-based war) will be better than traditional war (violence-oriented war) and will gain a foothold on this planet. In the 1990s IW included socialism and capitalism, peace and war, development and stagnation, cooperation and division, and survival and annihilation. If we are to eradicate war, we must first **control** war.

Chapter Six

The following is a 1989 speech titled "Some Thoughts on the Third World War." The place was not noted.

President Nixon did not mince words when he wrote in his book <u>1999: Victory Without War</u> that World War III began long before World War II ended. Victory without war requires that we resolve to use strength in ways short of war by engaging the enemy in the area of IW. It is hard to detect the soft knife behind the smokescreen of peace, and thus people lose vigilance. **Peaceful evolution strategy** reaches deep into a person's thoughts, undermines his political faith, and destroys his spiritual support. This softening strategy can lead to the self-division, self-strangulation, and self-dissolution of socialist countries.

Broadly defined, IW is a war in which opposing groups vie for information space and compete for information resources. It is the **hallmark of a deterrent war**. **Invisible information confrontation** includes strategic competition, theoretical deterrence, the battle for public opinion, potential confrontation, peaceful evolution, and counter-peaceful-evolution [Shen discussed these same issues in paragraph length in the previous chapter]. The **Western world's information strategy** is composed of a public opinion offensive and ideological infiltration, the cultivation of forces within the socialist countries to act as agents to whip up hostilities, the practice of economic coercion, and the practice of outright subversion and creation of all manner of division.

The Third World War will be a total information war. At the moment socialist countries are weak in the area of IW and must go on the defensive. But it must be an offense-oriented defense.

Chapter Seven

The following is an 11 December 1997 speech on military reform. The place was not listed. The chapter discusses military reform and is called "Accelerate the Push for an Information-based Army."

China needs an **information security commission**. Information security cannot be assured in the face of an **information invasion, information firepower surveillance, information deterrence, and information pollution**. Soldiers no longer have a patent on war. To check the deterrence capabilities of Western powers, China needs to develop weapons such as beam weapons, biological weapons, and super-computer virus weapons. The layers in the chain of command must be reduced. The high-level leadership management system and the system of colleges and universities must be reformed. China needs an information academy. The military should recruit directly from local college graduates. The intelligence system must be reorganized to become unified and comprehensive. There must be a reform of the defense economic system with a clean break between the military and business. The armed forces must put a complete stop to their involvement in procurement and business. The open-bidding system should be used in procurement of materials and equipment in order to help the logistic system. Finally, a mix of professional and compulsory conscription is needed. China should increase the proportion of volunteer soldiers and shorten the duration of compulsory military service. **Technology-intensive positions should be professionalized** and ordinary positions filled by conscripts.

Postscript

Dr. Shen wrote the Postscript to the book on 20 December 1999, almost a month after the Preface. It was written at Hangzhou. There was no indication that the Postscript had been part of a special presentation to a particular audience.

China, instead of building bigger and better, in the mid-1980s decided to place emphasis on economic construction and cut its army by one million men. At the same time the information age began to emerge, and as Nixon noted, there is a vast gray area between peace and war in which the struggle will be largely decided. If we expect to win without war, or even not to lose without war, we must engage the adversary within that area. The Third World War is full-fledged IW. This war is a long, drawn-out process. [Shen wrote this book to "examine world wars using IW theory" and to verify the feasibility of that theory.]

Only in 1995 did the country start to pay serious attention to IW. The reason it took so long was that the subject matter was sensitive at the time. The topics of peaceful evolution and counter-peaceful-evolution were evolving just as the events of 4 June 1989 unfolded, and there was also a "non-argument" period to contend with. Peaceful evolution and counter-peaceful-evolution can work with theories [stratagems]such as "Be relaxed on the outside while studying it intensively" and "Pay attention to it at the top while letting things go easy at the bottom." Such should be our strategy.

Most Americans see IW as a way of fighting. This is because they approach and apply IW mainly on a technical or purely military level (network attacks, hacking, computer viruses, precision assaults, electronic competition, etc.).

[This is the conclusion of Shen's book. It should be clear from his IW exposition that Shen is one of China's most brilliant IW specialists. His insights into IW deserve recognition for their candid exploration of the new and evolving territory of "IW with Chinese characteristics." Elements of Shen's influence on China's IW philosophy are visible throughout the chapter. Shen believes such theories as "attacking the enemy's knowledge system is more important than electronic confrontation" and "the purpose of war is control, not bloodshed" are gaining in popularity in America. The next chapter provides current thinking on IW developments in China (2000-2003).]

CHAPTER THREE: CHINESE INFORMATION-WAR THEORY AND PRACTICE 2001-2003

Introduction

Chinese open-source writings on information war were initially more reactive than proactive. Theorists discussed US definitions and concepts and studied results of coalition operations in the Gulf War and NATO operations during the fight for Kosovo. They worked diligently to describe the new situational context of the information age. At a meeting of Chinese IW specialists in 1997, the wheels were set in motion to begin a search for IW with Chinese characteristics. Between 1997 and the fall of 2000, several prominent theorists defined information operations and information war, described new training methods, discussed how information operations played a prominent role in training exercises, examined the impact of information operations on the Chinese theory of People's War, and discussed new roles for reserve forces, among other issues.

Now, as a result of work conducted over the period 2000-2003, a different type of discussion is unfolding in the open press.[112] China's military leaders are talking about a military transformation led by information-warfare themes. They are also talking about transforming the armed forces from a mechanized to an informationized force. Jiang Zemin, now the chairman of the Central Military Commission, pointed out in April 2003 that the essence of high-tech warfare is informationization and noted that IW will be the major form of warfare in the twenty-first century. Features of high-tech war will be its knowledge-oriented troops, intelligent weapons, integrated combat programs, digitized battlefield elements, precision-guided operational forms, multidimensional combat space, and intensive logistics support. Non-linear and noncontact operations will become the major combat forms of such wars. Further, Chinese theorists must study the training methods and tactics of IW. They must conduct simulated training, mock battles, and cyber-war drills. IW tactics must be turned into real fighting capacities.[113] The promotion of a reputed information warfare specialist (General Zhu Wenquan) to head the Nanjing military region, which faces Taiwan,[114] further underscores the IW emphasis in the PLA.

On 13 May 2003 the Communications Department of the General Staff held a seminar on military informationization to help implement Jiang Zemin's instructions. It was noted that informationization efforts must be aimed at winning future IW. Seminar participants concluded that China must build an IT-based weaponry system dominated by automated-command systems. It must also integrate command and control, intelligence, reconnaissance, early-warning monitoring, communication and electronic resistance, and precision fire attack systems into its combat theory, plus engage in coordinated offensive and defensive space operations.[115]

---

[112] Open source provides indicators or trends, but it does not provide confirmation of developments.

[113] http://www.pladaily.com.cn/gb/pladaily/2003/04/08/20030408001081_gdyl.html, from FBIS document CPP20030605000017.

[114] Fong,Tak-ho, "Princeling Promoted, as PLA Gets a Reshuffle," South China Morning Post, 22 November 2002, as translated and downloaded from the FBIS Web site on 22 November 2002.

[115] http://www.pladaily.com.cn/gb/pladaily/2003/05/13/20030513001131_gdyl.html, from FBIS document CPP20030605000017.

One dramatic change is that an increasing number of prominent Chinese military writers are focusing on the active offense (to include the creation of information forces). In the past the Chinese military was known for its focus on the active defense and their ability to transition to the offense from the active defense. They seldom, if ever, discussed the active offense (which implies taking the initiative) before 2000. The information age apparently has changed that approach. For example, the main Chinese IW proponent on the General Staff, Major General Dai Qingmin, stated in 2000 that in the age of IW the active offense is necessary if a nation wanted to maintain the initiative.[116]

Further, China's National Defense University published a book in 2001 that discussed the development of preemption strategies and the conduct of a "war of annihilation" strategy against enemy networks.[117] How and when these concepts might be used is unknown, but, as general concepts, they are worrisome. Some Chinese theorists openly state now that an opponent's information superiority can only be offset if China strikes first in a preemptive IW strike. They also argue that technology must be offset with innovative stratagems that deceive high-tech systems and force errors in the cognitive processes of opposing commanders.

Chinese IW specialists are offering fewer definitions of IW today, perhaps indicating that the debate over that issue has ended. Thus, it is clear that from 2000-2003 some conclusions were reached by the Chinese leadership regarding the nature of future war and IW's role in it. Clearly a growing emphasis was placed on expanding the use of IW as a part of Chinese war strategy. New topics were dominating the pages of military journals. Some of these topics included: an exploration of the concept of integrated network-electronic warfare (similar to the US concept of network-centric warfare), the identification of a growing number of IW units, the creation of new information warfare institutes that will serve as "aircraft carriers" of science and technology, the wartime mobilization potential of China's information technology industry, and thoughts on how to integrate technology with the ancient Chinese concept of stratagems. Real-world incidents, such as the hacker confrontation over the collision between a US EP-3 plane and a Chinese jet fighter, have affected Chinese IW perceptions as well. The number of IW related training exercises has risen sharply over the past five years. In short, China's IW theory is much more reflective of China's culture and traditions, and the requirements of the times, than it was some nine years ago.

China Military Science and Liberation Army Daily continued to be primary sources for Chinese IW articles. There are also a growing number of Chinese books on IW. Between 2000 and the end of 2003, for example, China Military Science has published at least (at the time of publication only five of the six editions of China Military Science in 2003 were available for review) over thirty articles on information

---

[116] Dai Qingmin, "Innovating and Developing Views on Information Operations," Zhongguo Junshi Kexue (China Military Science), August 2000, pp. 72-77 as translated and downloaded from the FBIS Web site.
[117] Ge Zhenfeng, The Science of Strategy, Strategic Research Department, Academy of Military Sciences, Military Science Press, Beijing, 2001.

related topics, and approximately ten articles on high-tech warfare. In addition to the major themes listed above, writers have also begun to write about military "informationization"[118] and the rationale for digitalization,[119] innovative thinking, closer civil-military integration in the information sector, movement from the mechanization age by "leaps and bounds" to the information age, and more emphasis on science and technology.

The Writing of Major General Dai Qingmin

If the debate over the concept of IW has ended, it is possible that Major General Dai had the last word on the subject. In three articles written between 2000 and 2003 he covered the definitions of IW, IO and information superiority (IS). There were only a limited number of definitions by other authors during the period, and few were authors of renown.

Dai listed six forms of IW: operational security, deception, computer network attack, electronic warfare, intelligence, and physical destruction. Dai singled out in particular electronic warfare and computer network warfare. He discussed the concept of "integrated network-electronic warfare (INEW)," similar in content to the US concept of network-centric warfare, in several of his articles. The concept refers to a series of combat operation actions that integrate EW and computer network warfare (CNW) means on the informationized battlefield. These means are designed to disrupt the normal operation of the enemy's battlefield network information systems, and protect one's own. Dai stated that the objective of INEW is to seize battlefield information superiority.[120]

Dai had earlier (2000) defined information operations as "a series of operations with an information environment as the basic battlefield condition, with military information and an information system as the direct operational target, and with electronic warfare and a computer network war as the principal forms."[121] In the same article he stated that contention for "information control" might become a focus of future war. Belligerents in a future war would contend for information superiority, but Dai

---

[118] Military informationization refers to the military area that relies on advanced information technology, equipment, and means to ceaselessly upgrade the capability of commanding military struggles and dominating military construction and operations in a step-by-step manner. It can be realized by developing information technology, improving information systems, and consolidating various military information systems into one. See Zhang Jianchang, "On Promoting the Informationization of the Chinese Military," Jiefangjun Bao (Liberation Army Daily), 28 January 2003 as translated and downloaded from the FBIS Web site on 6 February 2003.

[119] Xu Xiaoyan, Director of the Communication's Department of the General Staff, wrote in 2002 that digitalization is the early phase of informationization, to achieve effective and accurate information transmission. See Xu Xiaoyan, "A Concept for a Strategy of Development in which Informationization Drives Mechanization," Zhongguo Junshi Kexue (China Military Science), 1 February 2002, pp. 107-111 as downloaded and translated from the FBIS Web site on 10 September 2002.

[120] Dai Qingmin, "On Integrating Network Warfare and Electronic Warfare," Zhongguo Junshi Kexue (China Military Science), Feb 2002, pp. 112-117 as translated and downloaded from the FBIS Web site on 24 June 2002.

[121] Dai Qingmin, "Innovating and Developing Views on Information Operations."

maintained that information control was needed to create conditions for maintaining the initiative and winning final victory.[122]

Dai listed several characteristics of information supremacy:

- It is an integrated combat posture that can greatly affect the war as a whole.
- It allows freedom of movement in the information dimension and is conducted in three areas (electromagnetic space, computer network space, decision-makers' cognition and belief systems) and two levels (attack against information systems, attack against a human's cognition and belief systems).
- It influences events in the information dimension so as to affect events in the physical dimension.[123]

In 2002, also in the journal China Military Science, Major General Dai explained in more detail the "integrated network-electronic warfare" concept. Major General Dai's 2002 article was entitled "On Integrating Network Warfare and Electronic Warfare." It highlighted several topics of interest to Western information operations specialists, to include:[124]

- IO contradictions
- IO centers of gravity
- Network weaknesses
- The importance of IT training
- The method to create information superiority
- And definitions of information war and other terms, all with Chinese characteristics.[125]

Dai's 2002 article supported what he had written in 2000 on the active offense. This idea contradicted the 2002 China White Paper that continued to emphasize China's traditional active defense focus. Perhaps Dai's writings were for internal audiences whereas the White Paper was for foreign audiences. Dai also equated INEW with IO, which the White Paper did not do. Dai noted that INEW "serves as information operations theory with Chinese characteristics." He described INEW as reflective of Chinese culture and noted that INEW refers to an overall concept, method, and strategy for guiding IO. It does not refer to a set of hardware and software, or to a single system. It puts "the wings of network warfare on traditional electronic warfare." When discussing INEW's US equivalent, network-centric war, US theorists tend to use business metaphors (citing IBM and WalMart as examples), and they do not stress the electronic warfare and network warfare integration like the Chinese. Rather, US theorists point to the network's efficiency and speed as its key components, as well as the ability to move away from platform-oriented warfare.

---

[122] Ibid.
[123] Dai Qingmin, "On Seizing Information Supremacy," Zhongguo Junshi Kexue (China Military Science), April 2003, pp. 9-17, as translated and downloaded from the FBIS Web site.
[124] Dai Qingmin, "On Integrating Network Warfare and Electronic Warfare."
[125] Ibid.

While network war disrupts the opponent's processing and use of information, EW disrupts the opponent's acquisition and forwarding of information. The core of computer network warfare is to "disrupt the layers in which information is processed, with the objective of seizing and maintaining control of network space." EW is targeted at networked information systems and informationized weapons in order to increase combat effectiveness. INEW is essential for the system versus system confrontation on the informationized battlefield.[126]

INEW places emphasis on integrating combat operations elements of command, forces, objectives, and actions. Command integration is the unified planning, organization, coordination, and control of INEW. Force integration is the integrated use of INEW in a complementary manner. Objective integration is the simultaneous use of INEW against enemy C4ISR. Action integration is the coordination of INEW to produce combined power. Dai listed INEW's characteristics as its comprehensive nature, its integrated methods and expansive nature ("battle space"), and the integrated nature of its "effectiveness."[127]

INEW has a comprehensive effect on the enemy when it successfully *destroys* C4ISR, according to Dai, thereby constraining decision making and strategic planning. C4ISR systems are integrators and force multipliers. They are the focal points of IO according to Dai. He did not address what would happen if INEW only *damaged or disrupted* C4ISR, but one can imagine that the effects would be severe if not disabling. INEW's integrated methods can be developed into a unified plan and organization for action, and the expansive nature of battle space allows for noncontact and non-linear operations as well as full-depth, integrated attacks. Finally INEW's main targets are the enemy's military, political, economic, and social information systems making its potential effectiveness greater than any traditional combat operation form.[128]

Dai stated that China must transform its military focus from just electronic warfare to include network operations as represented by INEW. The emphasis in the information operations area, as represented by INEW, must be on acquiring both defensive and offensive information operations equipment "with the priority being the development of offensive information operations equipment." Further, it is "important to take the initiative and effectively destroy the enemy's electronic information systems...."[129] With regard to strategy, Dai noted that China must do the following:

- Make breakthroughs at weak points
- Seize the commanding high ground
- Leap out of dead ends and coordinate development
- And grasp key junctures.[130]

---

[126] Ibid.
[127] Ibid.
[128] Ibid.
[129] Ibid.
[130] Ibid.

To put the INEW plan into action will require the use of theoretical achievements, modeling of battlefield deployments, and other situational aspects of an enemy force. Perhaps this plan is being refined via training that utilizes computer network brigades and reserve IW units serving as Opposition Forces (OPFOR) against one another. In China, theory guides training, and rules and regulations are produced from an evaluation of the training.

Most likely, Dai's article was a condensed version of his book titled An Introduction to Integrated Network-Electronic Warfare. One Chinese critique of the book stated that the concept of INEW demonstrated that China no longer only learns from foreign militaries but also develops its own innovative theories with special Chinese military features. Further, the critique reiterated (as did Dai's 2002 article) that systems represent the center of gravity of combat forces, and that systems integration uses information as a control mechanism to form a combat capability greater than the sum of its parts.[131]

IW Units and the "Active Offense" in Chinese Military Thinking

There have been continuous open-source descriptions for three years of both cyber units and offensive cyber operations in the Chinese military and civilian press.[132] To understand this shift in emphasis chronologically, however, one needs to start with discussions in 1999. Zhu Wenguan and Chen Taiyi, in their book Information War , noted that preemptive active offense is needed to disrupt and destroy enemy computer offensive forces.[133] They also wrote that the PLA had established small brigades of offensive and defensive computer confrontation forces to conduct these attacks. These units study confrontation tactics and the psychological effects of computer confrontation. Confrontation tactics are defined as using forms and methods of confrontation in different situations. Computer confrontation has many variations. It can be used to destroy enemy C4I systems and to disable enemy command and control systems, to destroy enemy control systems of precision-guided weapons, to affect one's beliefs, to cause chaos in an enemy's information control system, to make an enemy disabled, or to weaken a side's combat potential and thus affect the course of a war.[134]

Information War noted that both offensive and defensive computer network brigades must be trained together using one another as a target. Training in computer confrontation is considered vital to success. China must teach leaders how to accurately organize, plan, and implement computer confrontation brigades.[135] Thus, Information Warfare implies that these units already exist and are practicing against one another.

---

[131] "Book Review: 'Introduction to Integrated Network-Electronic' Warfare," Jiefangjun Bao (Liberation Army Daily), 26 February 2002, p. 6, as translated and downloaded from the FBIS Web site on 26 February 2002. It is not known whether this book has been translated into English.

[132] See for example, Information War, Zhu Wenguan and Chen Taiyi, 1999, Chapter Five (Computer Operations). This chapter discusses offensive and defensive computer operations. No further information (publisher, etc.) was available.

[133] Ibid.

[134] Ibid.

[135] Ibid.

In November of 1999 a <u>PLA Daily</u> article stated that China may develop an IW branch of service—a "net force"—to complement the army, navy and air force. While the article stated that this development was very likely to become a reality, there is no evidence to confirm the creation of such a branch of service. Its task would be to protect net sovereignty and engage in net warfare. The latter included scanning technology, offensive and defensive technologies, "masquerade" (deception) technology, and recovery technology. Masquerade technology would assist a person who wanted to masquerade as a commander and take over a net. The article further noted that blind attacks and defense would not do since there must be technology, tactics, and the pursuit of actual effects when attacking and defending. In the future, in order to win, a nation must pursue coordinated land, sea, air, space, electronic, and net warfare.[136] Chinese authors did not mention a "net force" as a branch of service in their <u>2002 White Paper</u>.

In 2000, in an article in <u>China Military Science</u>, General Dai indicated that the offense was as important as the "active defense," and perhaps more so. He noted that "as the key to gaining the initiative in operations lies in positively and actively contending with an enemy for information superiority, China should establish such a view for IO as 'active offense.'" An active offense is the key to gaining information superiority, maintaining information control, and offsetting an opponent's superiority. Offensive information means can help sabotage an information system of an enemy.[137]

In a March 2000 Internet version of <u>Computer and Information Technology</u>, analysts at the PLA's Electronic Engineering Institute at Hefei discussed the need for network confrontation teams and their requirement to conduct both defensive and offensive operations.[138] In September 2000 the journal <u>Guangjiao Jing</u> noted that the PLA had recently established IW departments within its headquarters organizations.[139] In June 2002 Chinese author Wen T'ao described IW type units. He said these units were prepared to fight foreign attacks as well as to tamper "with information in terms of order, time, flow, content, and form; deleting information in parts, in order to create fragmented information; and inserting information to include irrelevant information in order to confuse and mislead each other."[140]

Wen added that two sides in a computer confrontation may try to destroy each other's information networks in order to paralyze information systems and prevent these systems from obtaining reliable information. Or they may attempt to invade each other's

---

[136] Leng Bingling, Wang Yulin, and Zhao Wenxiang, "Bringing Internet Warfare into the Military System is of Equal Significance with Land, Sea, and Air Power," <u>Jiefangjun Bao</u> (Liberation Army Daily), 11 November 1999, p. 7 as translated and downloaded from the FBIS Web site on 15 November 1999.
[137] Dai Qingmin, "Innovating and Developing Views on Information Operations."
[138] Yang Jian, Zhang Youhua, and Lu Zhankun, [no title], <u>Jisuanji Yu Xinxi Jishu</u> (Internet version of <u>Computer and Information Technology</u>), Anhui Computer Subscriber Association and the Anhui Computer Society, 16 March 2000 as translated and downloaded from the FBIS Web site on 18 April 2000.
[139] "China's IW Capabilities," <u>Guangjiao Jing</u>, Hong Kong, 16 September 2000.
[140] Wen T'ao, "PLA Bent on Seizing 'Information Control'," <u>Hong Kong Ching Pao</u>, 1 June 2002, Number 299, pp. 44-46 as translated and downloaded from the FBIS web page on 5 June 2002.

information networks by transplanting computer viruses to downloadable software that can be activated when necessary in order to sabotage each other's computer systems.

Wen suggested that China's IW units are under the command of the Confrontation Corps of a PLA General Staff Department that is charged with developing computer viruses and developing tactics for guarding PLA computer systems. There are units in various military regions that have undergone IW training in the past few years via several training exercises with notable results in both offensive and defensive fighting.[141]

The 2001 book Science of Strategy, published by China's National Defense University, also had a section that focused on offensive IW operations. The book noted that strategic IW should "use offense as a main strategy but be prepared for both offense and defense." Further, it stated "we should use the strategy of the preemptive strike and seize the initiative. Actively launching an information offensive is the key to seizing information superiority and the initiative on the battlefield."[142] The authors of Science of Strategy also underscored that "attention must be given to nurturing talent in information war and to establishing an 'informationalized' army" to satisfy the needs of future war.[143]

A January 2003 issue of Jiefangjun Bao called for enhancing China's capability to launch electronic and network-based warfare.[144] Finally, at the 2003 10th National People's Congress, PLA representatives offered the most convincing information on the existence of IW units. They revealed that the PLA is transitioning from mechanized units to high-tech information warfare units (IWU). The first such unit will be activated in Beijing in 2003, according to the report, and these units are being organized with computer specialists with high-tech expertise. The report stated that these units will eventually be in all PLA armies. IWUs will be outfitted with high-tech equipment, will have the ability to conduct network warfare on the Internet, and will have the capability to transfer data via remote sensing satellites.[145] How this "first" IW unit differs from the IW brigades under discussion in the 1999 Chinese book Information War is unknown. It does suggest that offensive IW units were discussed (and thus existed) in internal publications long before they were discussed publicly.

Little mention was made in open-sources of the IW role of specific reserve units' activities between the years 2000 to 2003. However the monthly journal of the PLA Academy of Military Science, Guofang, gave specific instructions in late 2003 on network attack activities to reserve units. Reserve forces must serve as an important component of People's War, author Li Mingrang stated, under the conditions of informatization. An auxiliary combat force system with People's War requirements must be built in China out of the reserves. Experts, professors, and the talent of local

---

[141] Ibid.

[142] Ge Zhenfeng, Chapter 16, Section 4, p. 366. For translations of excerpts of this book, the author thanks Dr. Gary Bjorge, Combat Studies Institute, Fort Leavenworth, Kansas.

[143] Ibid., p. 367.

[144] Zhang Jianchang. The author also stressed that a fundamental criterion of military informationization was the active defense strategy.

[145] "PLA to Organize First Information Warfare Units," Mingpao News, 12 March 2003, http://full.mingpaonews.com/20030312.

communications, telecommunications and financial departments, and scientific research institutes and institutions of higher education should be organized into reserve-duty militia units. Information storm troop "fist forces" must be established. Li called for the development of a "network People's War." Internet points must be developed that can be used directly for network combat in wartime as well as the stratagems to increase the systems survivability. The talent, technology, and resources to do so must be organized into modular groups beforehand. Training reserves to conduct such activities will increase the peace-to-war conversion capability of China.[146] Li added:

> Based on the new statistical findings of the State Ministry of Information Industry, there now are nearly twenty million network subscribers in China, and there is no shortage of computer experts and network jockeys among them, any one of whom could become a network guerrilla who could open up a gunpowderless battlefield all by himself by harassing attacks on the network, namely by releasing large volumes of data from many directions concentrated on some enemy network station to jam up its network router and bring the network station to a standstill…and once there is a military requirement, either enter the network system to steal intelligence, or to activate viruses or detonate 'bombs' to achieve the combat target of destroying the network….[147]

Thus it is clear that reserve forces continue to play an important role in PLA IW planning, and that they too are directed to work on offensive strategies. Network attacks appear to be a popular topic across the board in Chinese writings.

In the PLA IW-related exercises listed later in this chapter, several contained references to computer network attacks, cyber attacks, and offensive IW. Thus, the open source literature quite clearly discusses both the theory and practice of the conduct of offensive IW, and often points to the creation of specialized units. In February of 2003 the US Strategic Command announced its plans to develop a network attack task force as part of its reorganization. Perhaps for this reason China decided to announce its own units at the March 2003 People's Congress.

There was also much discussion in the Chinese press about defensive organizations designed to thwart an enemy information attack and to uncover loopholes in the current network system. For example, an August 2000 article published by the Zhongguo Tongxun She news agency discussed the creation of an antihacking force.[148]

Network Operations Will Be a "War of Annihilation"

Major General Dai offered a further explanation of INEW in a December 2002 article. He wrote:

---

[146] Li Mingrang, "Develop the Advantage of People's War under the Conditions of Innovation and Informatization," Guofang, 15 November 2003, pp. 7-8 as translated and downloaded from the FBIS Web site.
[147] Ibid.
[148] "China has a Special Force of Members Who Possess Intimidating Qualifications," Zhongguo Tongxun She News Agency, Hong Kong, 22 August 2000, obtained via e-mail from internetcrimenews@infowar.com.

The scientific pronouncement of Chairman Jiang that in the main the construction of information warfare means the construction of electronic warfare and computerized network warfare profoundly reveals the natural characteristics and core content of information warfare, and locates the prominent breakthrough points and focal points of our energies in the construction and development of military information warfare. Information warfare is an effective method to be used to attack the combat systems supported by information systems to bring about their complete destruction.[149]

Regarding the integrating nature of IW, Dai noted that informationized weapons platforms (is this China's NCW equivalent?) are composed of information systems formed into networks that unite an entire combat system into one integrated "structure of information."[150] He also noted that military force used after the application of electronic warfare has a coefficient multiplied by nine times and if more electronic warfare methods are used simultaneously, then "the multiplication of the coefficient of military force will actively increase accordingly."[151] This will enable IW to bring about the total destruction of information systems that is the most characteristic method of attack in the information age.[152] Thus EW holds a place of prominence in Dai's six forms of IW.

In addition to General Dai's ideas on integrated network-electronic operations, Chinese books and journals have carried several other discussions on network operations, indicating its growing importance to Chinese theorists.[153] Jiefangjun Bao, for example, carried an article in August of 2002 about the forms of network attacks. These were listed as premeditated (i.e., a persistent computer viruses embedded in software), contamination (aimed at the quality of information), strong (refers to the forced modulation of computer viruses into electromagnetic waves) and fission (the strong regeneration capability of a virus). Active defense network methods were listed as blocking the attack at the source (inspections or monitors), actively responding to interference and reconnaissance (not only to augment protection measures, but also to introduce deception and interference measures), keeping the enemy out of the network (by controlling knowledge of core systems and the codes and passwords of important users), and augmenting intrinsic "immunity" (cultivating network soldiers for the future, and continuously improving the ability to discern enemy actions and establish back-up data banks so that normal operations can be quickly restored after damage).

The 2001 book Science of Strategy described the type of war to be fought against networks. The book stated that a war of annihilation, as opposed to traditional mobile

---

[149] Dai, Qingmin, "On the Development of Army Informationization and Information Warfare," Zhongguo Junshi Kexue (China Military Science), Number 6, 2002, pp. 66-70 as translated and downloaded from the FBIS Web site on 20 December 2002.
[150] Ibid.
[151] Ibid.
[152] Ibid.
[153] Fan Yongsheng, Wu Xinghan, "War on Networks: Modern 'Contradictory' Offensive, Defensive Warfare," Jiefangjun Bao (Liberation Army Daily), 14 August 2002, p. 11 as translated and downloaded from the FBIS Web site on 14 August 2002.

war, position war, or guerrilla war, is more suitable for China's armed forces. In a war of annihilation, nodes must be attacked to break up the network. One must destroy the enemy's brain and central nervous system, and this can happen through attacks against structures and procedures of the enemy's operational systems, according to the book's authors. Attacks should be directed against nodes that sustain the enemy's war system and against weak points that are hard to replace or regenerate and result in unstoppable chaos. Another focus should be capitalizing on an enemy's loss of operational balance. Information systems and support systems must always be the first targets and then the stronger weapon systems. Science of Strategy notes that "after strikes to damage the net and continuous operations and persistent weakening of the enemy, then vigorously launch an annihilating attack." Ground facilities, information transmission means, perception platforms, and information flow capabilities should be destroyed in that order. This enables one to "take away the firewood from under the cauldron."[154]

The PLA recognizes that a battlefield military information network is vastly different from business or public networks and from military office networks. US analysts, on the other hand, continue to draw comparisons between business's efficiency and the need for similar efficiency and speed in the military as reflected in the concept of network-centric war. For China, the aim of a battlefield information network is to create an environment in which it can win a high-tech war of medium or large scale and use stratagems to do so. A military information network "represents an information territory or sovereignty; to an army, it represents a front where servicemen perform their duties; to military strategy, it represents a battlefield for information war; and to war, it represents an important material basis or a key means for a war's conduct."[155]

In February of 2003 another report indicated that network training is ongoing. The Shenyang Military Region reportedly worked on new tactics to direct their network-based training by organizing "successive network-based maneuvers under conditions very close to reality and actual combat." The unit also has strengthened network construction, developed software training facilities, and intensified network-based training to meet the requirements of the "New Outline of Military Training and Evaluation" indicating that this is probably an army-wide effort. Both blue and red army forces were used in the training.[156]

Five New IW Institutes and IW Education

One of the most repeated themes in Chinese military educational circles has been the call for more innovative thinking among scientists. Innovation is necessary in military theory, technology, and operational methods. First steps in this direction have been taken at the Academy of Information Engineering of the University of Information Engineering

---

[154] Ge Zhenfeng, Chapter 24, Section 6, p. 493.

[155] Chen Ting, "From Informationalizing Units to Informationalized Units," Jiefangjun Bao, 5 December 2000 p. 6 as translated and downloaded from the FBIS Web site on 3 December 2000.

[156] "A Certain Unit of the Shenyang Military Region Improves Command Tactics for Network-Based Military Training," Jiefangjun Bao (Liberation Army Daily) (Internet Version), 9 February 2003, as translated and downloaded from the FBIS Web site on 24 February 2003.

of the People's Liberation Army. The academy reportedly introduced the following into their curriculum in 2002:

- Two undergraduate courses: Space Information and Network Engineering
- A mobile postdoctoral research station in Information and Communications Engineering
- A doctoral degree in Information and Communications Engineering and in Signal and Information Processing
- Master's degree programs in Computer System Structure and Military Operations Research.[157]

Major General Zhou Xiaokun of the university believes that such courses will enhance creativity and innovation among new officers while updating teaching methodologies. He views innovation as the core of the knowledge-based economy and educational reform.[158]

This emphasis on technology and innovation is also seen in new information-related PLA institutes. China's Xinhua News Agency reported the creation in September 2002 of a new set of five research institutes to boost China's information warfare capability. The newest is located in the northern city of Zhengzhou. Other centers are in Beijing, Xian, and Nanjing, meaning either that one of those could have two centers, or that one center was not named. These science and technology workstations are "technology aircraft carriers" that reportedly employ thousands of specialists and contain thousands of advanced machines in hundreds of labs. Xinhua News reports that these work stations are directly administered by the PLA General Staff Headquarters.[159]

Military leaders at these institutes are expected to work on innovative IW methods and forms of warfare. China wants to overcome their technological backwardness with "asymmetric warfare" attacks against technologically superior foes. To accomplish this they will use computer attacks, electronic interference and other information warfare techniques.[160]

PLA Training and Training Exercises

Perhaps the most significant exercise with IW implications was the Dongshan Island exercise in April of 2001. The exercise was held just opposite Taiwan, increasing its importance to the Pacific region and the US in general. The Taiwanese reported that the exercise's first phase started with an information warfare focus. One report noted that a joint electronic countermeasure maneuver was conducted using new technology and operational methods, such as interference, deception, and precision strikes. Senior

---

[157] Zhou Xiaokun, "How Should Military Academies Conduct Innovative Education," Guangming Ribao, (Internet Version), 14 January 2003 as translated and downloaded from the FBIS Web site on 14 January 2003.
[158] Ibid.
[159] "Mainland Boosts 'Information Warfare' Centers," China Post, 28 September 2002.
[160] Ibid.

officers were required to engage in online confrontation.[161] The key task was to take electronic countermeasures to paralyze enemy communication and command systems.[162] Another report stated that the exercise marked the first time that a PLA special electronics confrontation force operated in coordination with military surveillance satellites above the Taiwan Strait.[163] Other exercises that included IW have subsequently been held. In September 2002, for example, the Shanghai Garrison prepared to conduct an IW exercise and, during the actual exercise, viruses were countered according to reports.

Each year hundreds of exercises are conducted in China that go unreported in the Western press, and many have IW overtones. It is clear when reading summaries of the exercises that nearly every branch of service has been touched. The list includes armor, air defense, weather and mapping personnel, logistics, psychological warfare, the Navy and Air Force, the Second Artillery Corps, and the militia.

IW training held in the year 2003 is the focus of this section. More than forty-three exercises are listed on the following pages. The exercises are divided by military region. The results here depict the fact that the Lanzhou, Shenyang, and Beijing military regions conducted more IW exercises than the other regions. Interestingly, the Nanjing military region opposite Taiwan reported very few exercises. It is not known if more exercises were conducted in this region but not reported due to their sensitivity. However, the exercises do indicate that IW training has become an integral component of the PLA's training plan for the foreseeable future.

Beijing

15 April—An unspecified artillery brigade conducted high-tech training. It tried to master the "three striking items" and the "three defending items." The former included striking at stealth planes, cruise missiles, and armored helicopters and the latter included defending against precision attacks, electronic interference, and detecting reconnaissance assets of the opposition. The brigade also trained in electronic interference, counterelectronic interference, countersatellite reconnaissance, counterelectronic reconnaissance, and logistics support.[164]

17 May—An unspecified group army intensified the construction of its mapping detachment and built this detachment into a key logistical force for IW. It educated its troops on theories of joint operations and IW.[165]

---

[161] Chen Tung-lung, "Secret Intelligence: Summary of Exercises Shows the Purpose is to Attack the Island and Strike at Warships," Taipei Tung-sen Hsin-Wen Pao, 3 March 2002 as translated and downloaded from the FBIS Web site on 6 March 2002.

[162] Peng Kai-lei, "At the Head of 100 Generals, Zhang Wannian Takes Command of Zhangzhou Defense Personally," Hong Kong Wen Wei Po, 10 July 2001 as translated and downloaded from the FBIS Web site on 10 July 2001.

[163] "More on PRC Report on PLA Strategies Employed during Dongshan Island Exercises," Shanghai Guoji Zhanwang, 1 July 2001 p. 12, as translated and downloaded from the FBIS Web site on 1 July 2001.

[164] http://www.pladaily.com.cn/gb/pladaily/2003/04/15/20030415001006_TodayNews.html, from FBIS document CPP20030512000067.

[165] http://www.pladaily.com.cn/gb/pladaily/2003/05/15/20030515001122_Army.html, from FBIS document CPP20030701000076.

12 June—An unspecified Chinese regiment organized its squads to view and emulate its division's demonstrations on a network-based, mock tactical battle. Audio-video aids helped conduct the training that used the local area network to educate troops and assess commanders' and staff officers' theoretical and tactical qualities.[166]

23 July—Communications maneuvers were conducted that featured electromagnetic interference, stealth operations, and antireconnaissance maneuvers.[167]

24 September—An unspecified signal station developed a system for checking and managing long-distance optical fiber cables and a high frequency, thunder-resistant system. With these systems technicians can check communication equipment hundreds of kilometers away.[168]

11 October—An unspecified division held its annual military rehearsal to review its information-based operational command systems and basic electronic warfare tactics. The division set up digitized transmission lines and wireless networks and utilized unmanned reconnaissance vehicles to gather battlefield information.[169]

14 October—The "blue army" immediately launched electronic assaults against the command and control center of the "red army" in a signal detachment exercise. Red took electronic defensive measures to protect its networks. Blue then used advanced IW equipment to launch all-directional electromagnetic intercepts and closed "red's" communication networks. Red then used camouflaged communication networks to transmit documents, images, and sound data to the operational command headquarters.[170]

17 November—An IW drill was held at the command-training center. The "red" and "blue" armies launched reconnaissance activities to detect each other. They mobilized their digitized tanks, missiles, and stealth fighters to exchange fires and make precision assaults. First Secretaries of the party committees of some military sub-districts attended this drill.[171]

Nanjing

2 April—A tactical training drill named Huai He 2003 near Anhui included "tens of computers applied to swiftly handle the information from the battlefield." Commanders applied modern information technology to analyze and handle the information related to the enemy as well as the latest maps and meteorological and hydrological data of the combat zone. The armies engaged in fierce reconnaissance and counterreconnaissance, air raids and counterair raids, and infiltration and counterinfiltration battles, as well as electromagnetic interference measures.[172]

[166] http://www.pladaily.com.cn/gb/pladaily/2003/06/12/20030612001013_Army.html, from FBIS document CPP20030605000017.
[167] http://www.pladaily.com.cn/gb/pladaily/2003/07/23/20030723001083_Army.html, from FBIS document CPP20030821000146.
[168] http://www.pladaily.com.cn/gb/pladaily/2003/09/24/20030924001133_Army.html, from FBIS document CPP20031104000025.
[169] http://www.pladaily.com.cn/gb/pladaily/2003/10/11/20031011001018_Army.html, from FBIS document CPP20031106000001.
[170] http://www.pladaily.com.cn/gb/pladaily/2003/10/14/20031014001018_Army.html, from FBIS document CPP20031106000001.
[171] http://www.pladaily.com.cn/gb/pladaily/2003/11/17/20031117001032_Army.html, from FBIS document CPP20031204000020.
[172] http://www.pladaily.com.cn/gb/pladaily/2003/04/02/20030402001199_Army.html, from FBIS document CPP20030410000103.

24 November—In a mock war, communication systems crashed and the national defense mobilization command network promptly switched to transmit orders to lower levels. The Nanjing City National Defense Mobilization Committee conducted this exercise based on new high-tech equipment.[173]

Shenyang

20 March—An unspecified regiment carried out network-based training with the support of local field command networks. The regiment intensified the study of modern command knowledge and technology with information technology as its core.[174]

6 July—An unspecified division integrated its IT-based resources and developed an automatic combat command system. The division invited more than thirty specialists and scholars to lecture on IW theories and tactics. The control center deployed over ten sets of automatic army tactical command systems to this division.[175]

29 July—Technicians from Firstlink Digital Technology Company Limited traveled to a unit in Shenyang Military Region to provide high-tech teaching materials.[176]

14 August—The Sixth Company of an unspecified artillery division trained with IT, and it utilized new methods and tactics. These included strong electronic interference, counterjamming, cyber attacks, and countercyber attacks. The unit also trained in gathering, storing, analyzing, processing, and sending battlefield information.[177]

9 August—An unspecified army group headquarters organized electron warfare, reconnaissance, meteorological, and antichemical warfare. An electronic warfare battalion launched electronic jamming against a combat system of the command post.[178]

31 August—A "blue army" equipped with IW command platforms and electronic-jamming systems was countered by a "red army" that used microwave video transmission systems (and back-up command systems).[179]

22 September—An unspecified division applied systems integration, satellite communications, data extraction and encryption, and computer network control technologies during a field operation. It also held combat meetings via networks.[180]

12 October—An unspecified artillery regiment conducted a tactical drill under high-tech conditions. Commanders at various levels conducted reconnaissance by firing and

---

[173] http://www.pladaily.com.cn/gb/pladaily/2003/11/24/20031124001224_Army.html, from FBIS document CPP20031204000020.

[174] http://www.pladaily.com.cn/gb/pladaily/2003/003/20/20030320001011_Army.html, from FBIS document CPP20030409000119.

[175] http://www.pladaily.com.cn/gb/pladaily/2003/08/14/20030814001005_TodayNews.html, from FBIS document CPP20030716000017.

[176] http://www.pladaily.com.cn/gb/pladaily/2003/0729/20030729001029_Army.html, 29 July 2003.

[177] http://www.pladaily.com.cn/gb/pladaily/2003/07/20/20030720001002_Army.html, from FBIS document CPP20030821000146.

[178] http://www.pladaily.com.cn/gb/pladaily/2003/08/09/20030809001013_TodayNews.html, from FBIS document CPP20030912000151.

[179] http://www.pladaily.com.cn/gb/pladaily/2003/08/31/20030831001010_TodayNews.html, from FBIS document CPP20031008000192.

[180] http://www.pladaily.com.cn/gb/pladaily/2003/09/22/20030922001012_TodayNews.html, from FBIS document CPP20031104000025.

launched electronic jamming while taking preventive measures against reconnaissance, electronic jamming, and computer network attacks.[181]

3 December—At an unspecified training base, the command communication system's self-defense capabilities were stressed. Attention was also paid to integrating offensive with defensive tactics, and efforts were made to explore computer network investigation techniques, node sabotage, and information assault techniques and tactics. The goal is to allow information systems to be capable of carrying out both offensive and defensive operations.[182]

Jinan

Mid-May—An unspecified army group conducted a high-tech OPFOR exercise using the information processing equipment of a subordinate unit. The aim of the exercise was to enhance command capabilities of IW. It is reported that nearly 80% of the officer cadre can "accurately control the group army's information systems."[183]

30 May—A mechanized infantry brigade was recently renovated, promoting command automation, informationization of weaponry, and IT. The brigade will require high-tech detachments to transform its informationized equipment into a combat effective force.[184]

16 July—Since May the paper Qianwei Bao (Vanguard Newspaper) of the Jinan Military Region has run a column on servicemen's procurement of personal computers and their hope to access the Internet. Computer use was even encouraged by a political commissar from Unit No. 72253. Computer mastery will help China's military realize military modernization with information technology. Servicemen were also warned to avoid disclosure of confidential information and to follow proper operational security procedures.[185]

22 August—An unspecified group army held a joint operational drill designed to enhance its IW capabilities. The group army invited specialists and professors from neighboring units. It introduced other units' scientific findings, such as the Second Artillery Corps' "new camouflage system" and an air unit's "data compatible controller." In 2003 the unit organized more than ten cyber war drills together with its neighboring army units.[186]

7 September—An unspecified artillery brigade conducted a drill under high-tech conditions that included electronic jamming. The jamming disconnected the radio stations of all units so the companies reconnected using civilian communications lines.[187]

---

[181] http://www.pladaily.com.cn/gb/pladaily/2003/10/12/20031012001011_Army.html, from FBIS document CPP20031106000001.

[182] Zhang Zili and Gao Jianlin, "Let Command Communications Acquire a Modern War Tempo—the Command Communications' Transformation to Become Combat-Ready as Demonstrated in Maneuvers Conducted in a Certain Training Base in the Shenyang Military Region," Jiefangjun Bao (Liberation Army Daily) (Internet version), 3 December 2003, p. 9 as translated and downloaded from the FBIS Web site on 20 December 2003.

[183] PLA Daily News, 9 June 2003.

[184] http://www.pladaily.com.cn/gb/pladaily/2003/05/30/20030530001013_TodayNews.html, from FBIS document CPP20030605000017.

[185] http://www.pladaily.com.cn/gb/pladaily/2003/07/16/20030716001121_Army.html, from FBIS document CPP20030819000043..

[186] http://www.pladaily.com.cn/gb/pladaily/2003/08/22/20030822001005_TodayNews.html, from FBIS document CPP20030912000151.

[187] http://www.pladaily.com.cn/gb/pladaily/2003/079/07/20030907001006_Army.html, from FBIS document CPP20031008000192.

9 September—Ten specialists from the General Staff gathered with some army and division leaders from the Jinan Military Region to assess the technological integration of information and weaponry systems developed by this group army over the past few years. More than twenty applied software programs were developed, such as the program to monitor the mobility of troops and the program to assess destructive effects. The field command control system and electronic warfare system were integrated. Information transmission and processing capabilities improved dramatically.[188]

Chengdu

23 January—Air Defense Forces conducted computer-based, simulated tactical training on new computer networks and control systems.[189]

9 February—Zhang Yu used new software to build a network protection center and created counterhacking programs for the Chengdu Military Region.[190]

20 August—An unspecified unit conducted field maneuvers and used mobile communications and satellite communications equipment. The unit employed photoelectronic and radar electronic warfare means.[191]

21 September—An unspecified division organized a mock war at its simulated training hall. The "blue army" used reconnaissance satellites and advanced electronic reconnaissance means. The "red army" launched counterjamming and counterreconnaissance attacks along with psychological warfare and fire attacks.[192]

27 November—"Blue army" units, which consisted of electronic confrontation units, special reconnaissance units, and communication units, attacked "red army" units. The latter reportedly suffered in the first few minutes of the fight as its automatic command system was initially paralyzed. Lessons were learned, it was reported, from the launching of offensive and defensive cyber, electronic, and fire strike attacks against one another.[193]

Lanzhou

28 January—A group army installed information networks for military training and training centers. It used a remote-controlled interactive simulation system to command long-distance battlefields and to transmit information to battlefields through information networks. This army has built a modernized communication-training base with more than ten audio-visual classrooms so that all communication detachments can take turns on specialized training equipment.[194]

---

[188] http://www.pladaily.com.cn/gb/pladaily/2003/09/09/20030909001029_Army.html, from FBIS document CPP20031104000025.

[189] http://www.pladaily.com.cn/gb/pladaily/2003/01/23/20030123001021_Army.html, from FBIS document CPP20030203000055

[190190] http://www.pladaily.com.cn/gb/pladaily/2003/02/09/20030209001010_Army.html, from FBIS document CPP20030313000039.

[191] http://www.pladaily.com.cn/gb/pladaily/2003/08/20/20030820001011_TodayNews.html, from FBIS document CPP20030821000146.

[192] http://www.pladaily.com.cn/gb/pladaily/2003/09/21/20030921001027_Army.html, from FBIS document CPP 20031008000192.

[193] Zheng Xin and Chen Banghe, "Chengdu MAC Caries out Information Warfare Drills on Plateau," Jiefangjun Bao (Liberation Army Daily), 27 November 2003 as translated and downloaded from the FBIS Web site on 27 November 2003.

[194] http://www.pladaily.com.cn/gb/pladaily/2003/01/28/20030128001021_Army.html, from FBIS document CPP20030203000055

25 March—An unspecified division reported conducting training for staff officers in the operation and using of automatic command system, computer virus attacks, data backup, and firewall technologies. More than 95% of the staff officers at or above the division and regiment levels have mastered computer-related techniques.[195]

11 May—A group army organized simulated battles. They initially installed high-quality "blue army" detachments capable of taking part in IW in each regimental-level unit. This group helped the "red army" make new headways in cyber warfare drills and simulated battles.[196]

16 May—An elite mechanized infantry division in the Lanzhou Military Region conducted a network OPFOR Exercise (the exercise took place in April and was reported in May). The division utilized more than ten electronic-warfare tactical subjects. It functions as both a hard-kill and soft-kill unit.[197]

27 May—An unspecified armored regiment organized a simulated battle in conjunction with real troops. It was noted that "with the new armored vehicles serving as platforms, wireless data networks as carriers, and combat command circuits as the main lines, this regiment conducted transformation and re-assemble of its equipment and initially set up an information technology-based combat system." The regiment has technologically renovated its joint combat command systems, armored reconnaissance systems, and traditional communications networks. The regiment's combat command systems, reconnaissance, monitoring, information-processing command and control, and overall logistics functions are interconnected with one another as a result.[198]

8 July—An unspecified signal regiment has "in line with the special features of high-tech warfare and IW, built combat training platforms; built simulated training rooms, computer classrooms, system simulation classrooms, and psychological-warfare classrooms; connected the information networks of all companies via the Internet; upgraded the real-time command and control system; and built, step by step, auxiliary training and logistics support facilities" to meet the needs of IW.[199]

20 July—Maneuvers in the desert featured jamming and counterjamming, reconnaissance and antireconnaissance, and deception and counterdeception. The maneuvers observed the laws of military operations under high-tech conditions and involved intelligence gathering, situational analysis, decision making, and command operations.[200]

22 October—An unspecified artillery regiment held a tactical war drill. Tens of computers were used to rapidly process the information from the battlefield. Numbers of tanks were known simply by clicking on a computer mouse.[201]

---

[195] http://www.pladaily.com.cn/gb/pladaily/2003/03/25/20030327001022_Army.html, from FBIS document CPP20030401000170.

[196] http://www.pladaily.com.cn/gb/pladaily/2003/05/11/20030511001029_Army.html, from FBIS document CPP20030602000013.

[197] Oriental Daily http://orientaldaily.com.hk/new/new_c54cnt.html, 16 May 2003; also PLA Daily at http://pladaily.com.cn/gb/pladaily/2003/05/15/20030515001024_TodayNews.html, 15 May 2003.

[198] http://www.pladaily.com.cn/gb/pladaily/2003/05/27/20030528001025_Army.html, from FBIS document CPP20030602000013.

[199] http://www.pladaily.com.cn/gb/pladaily/2003/07/08/20030708001028_Army.html, from FBIS document CPP20030716000017.

[200] http://www.pladaily.com.cn/gb/pladaily/2003/07/20/20030720001002_Army.html, from FBIS document CPP20030821000146.

[201] http://www.pladaily.com.cn/gb/pladaily/2003/10/22/20031022001122_Army.html, from FBIS document CPP20031104000025.

12 November—An unspecified radar regiment of the Lanzhou Military Region Air Force conducted a two-week long IW support exercise. An unspecified motorized maneuver element traveled 3600 kilometers while performing training for IW countermeasures such as setting up radar sites in secrecy, and conducting airspace intelligence support and anti-air jamming. The exercise improved the unit's IW operational capabilities.[202]

20 November—A PLA brigade in Tibet recently conducted an offensive /defensive exercise in PSYWAR. The "red army" used acousto-optic interference units and other PSYWAR devices to jam the equipment of the "blue army." This demonstrated the capability to launch both offensive and defensive PSYWAR.[203]

24 December—Five computer installed in a "red army" command post were jammed by a "blue army" electronic detachment. The "red army" forces launched electronic jamming against the "blue army" computer networks, and reported the situation via automated command systems.[204]

Guangzhou

3 May—An unspecified air unit of the Guangzhou Military Region in conjunction with the South Sea Fleet held a simulated war drill to practice counterinterference and ultra-low-altitude assault tactics. Electronic interference was utilized against the air units, and the latter conducted counterinterference tactics against the four corvettes in the region.[205]

20 August—An unspecified communications regiment conducted maneuvers under high-tech conditions using strong electromagnetic interference, digital program controls, satellite communications, and counterjamming measures such as frequency conversion and frequency hopping to allow the rapid transmission of textual, video, and audio data to command posts.[206]

18 September—An unspecified mechanized division studied IW theories, IW tactics, and IT. It intensified the transformation of existing equipment in order to transform IW tactics and training achievements into troop operational warfare drills. During the training, electromagnetic interference, electron feints, and precision attacks on the battlefield were conducted.[207]

25 September—A missile brigade allocated 60,000 Yuan to procure software for systems in order to promote IT in the unit. The brigade had already invested in video-telephone systems, communication lines to remote areas, and local area networks.[208]

---

[202] China Com Military News, http://military.china.com/zh_cn/news/568/20031112/11569617.html, 12 November 2003.

[203] PLA Daily, http://www.pladaily.com.cn/gb/pladaily/2003/11/20/2003112001028_Army.html, 20 November 2003.

[204] http://www.pladaily.com.cn/gb/pladaily/2003/12/24/20031224001023_Army.html, from FBIS document CPP20040105000199.

[205] http://orientaldaily.com.hk/new_c06cnt.html, from FBIS document CPP20030516000141.

[206] http://www.pladaily.com.cn/gb/pladaily/2003/08/20/20030820001012_TodayNews.html, from FBIS document CPP20030821000146.

[207] http://www.pladaily.com.cn/gb/pladaily/2003/09/18/20030918001023_Army.html, from FBIS document CPP20031104000025.

[208] Guangzhou Zhanshi Bao, 25 September 2003, from FBIS document CPP20031104000025.

Information Mobilization: Permeating All "Mob" Areas

Chinese military specialists are aware of the growing importance of information resources during the transition from the mechanization age of weaponry into the information age. They are also aware of the growing integration of military and civilian industries in the information age and the consequent importance of a capability to mobilize information assets. Major General Xu Xiaoyan, head of the General Staff's Communications Department, believes that China must "study the special characteristics and norms of information resources development, accelerating information infrastructure development and creating an information resource mobilization mechanism" to help China "fight to win."[209] Xu added that an information society is now composed of information industries, information resources and economies, and information networks. IW is the fight with and for these resources that must be harnessed and incorporated into China's mobilization plan for war. The information age caused this closer coordination between military and civilian resources. Information mobilization actions include strengthening the mobilization awareness of citizens since even nonmilitary personnel can use a computer as an operational platform for IW. Information attacks in peacetime can cause social disorder and achieve the art of "winning without fighting."[210]

> All locations where networks can extend will become IW battlefields. No matter if it is the citizens of any country, no matter what locality, as long as they possess certain computer knowledge and master certain network attack skills, they can then apply the mouse under their thumb to war on the network, enabling the global nature of IW.[211]

According to Xu mobilization today is not like mobilization trends of traditional wars. No longer do countries wait for war to be thrust upon them. Information mobilization must be conducted in peacetime. With computers it is possible to "not be peaceful during peacetime" and to prepare the country for any potential scenario. During peacetime, networks and mobilization plans should be strengthened to further enable networks to assist economic policy and national security. Victory in an information war will result from the successful control and application of information resources and from obtaining and controlling command and control over information.[212]

Xu closed his article by suggesting that China should establish an information resource mobilization office responsible for the planning and organization of the country's information resource mobilization; the command decision-making, inspection, and supervision process; organizational coordination; and legal work. Further, all military theaters and all provinces, cities, and autonomous regions should establish corresponding agencies. Other recommendations by Xu were to formulate and establish a talented

---

[209] Xu Xiaoyan, "Establishing an Information Resource Mobilization Mechanism with Chinese Characteristics," Zhongguo Junshi Kexue (China Military Science), 20 October 2000, pp. 77-82, 95 as translated and downloaded from the FBIS web page on 5 December 2000.
[210] Ibid.
[211] Ibid.
[212] Ibid.

information reserve mobilization program, an IW education program, and an information network resource mobilization program.[213]

The information resource mobilization program would be carried out under the socialist market economic system and not under the socialist planned economic system. Thus policies, laws, and systems must be perfected. Recommended laws included the following:

- Law of information resource mobilization
- Law for information network resource mobilization
- Law for information security for management
- Law for information reserve personnel mobilization
- Law for information technical reserve mobilization
- Law for information education resources mobilization and
- Law for information material resource mobilization.[214]

Guofang, another journal of the Academy of Military Science, published an article in 2001 by Major General Hua Binglai that supported Xu's basic findings. Hua contended that information mobilization had already become a new aspect of national defense mobilization, permeating all mobilization areas. This included the People's Armed Police mobilization, national economic mobilization, transportation war preparation mobilization, and people's air defense mobilization. Hua underscored the new importance attached to psychological-warfare operations. Psychological-warfare operations heighten the importance of national defense mobilization in the age of information when an enemy can reach out to China's populace in a way never before imagined.[215]

Other authors have also written on the subject of information mobilization. One stressed the importance of mobilizing information technology and telecommunication industries in order to lay a foundation for expediting the informationization of the armed forces. Managers and specialists in information technology who stood out on the information industrial front must be organized to help safeguard the military during time of IW. Author Zhou Tao closed by noting that China had "brought all information-related services and systems into the orbit of wartime, with the view of mobilizing all national and social information resources to serve national security and warfare, and guarantee the command of information."[216]

Continuing this mobilization trend, in the autumn of 2001 Shangai's National Defense Mobilization Committee reportedly established an Information Mobilization

---

[213] Ibid.

[214] Ibid.

[215] Hua Binglai, [no title given], Guofang, 15 January 2001, pp. 11-12 as translated and downloaded from the FBIS web page on 6 March 2001.

[216] Zhou Tao, "Military Informationization," Jiefangjun Bao (Liberation Army Daily), 23 December 2002, as translated and downloaded from the FBIS Web site on 6 February 2003.

Office and an information resources platform or duty station.[217] Over a year later (2003), another report stated that the scientific and technological mobilization trend in all countries is moving towards combining production for peacetime and wartime use thus causing more integration between the military and civilian sectors. New combat tactics must appear for People's War under modern conditions as a result. This includes reinforcing links between mobilization organs of the same level, and between civilian and military sectors. The desire is to create a synchronous and real-time coordination mechanism for a mobilization command featuring reliable communications. Joint military-civilian war exercises would be organized as well to improve and perfect preplans for mobilization and to test mobilization capacities.[218]

People's War and Information Militias

The People's War concept received a renewed interpretation in the 2000-2003 period. Writer Che Hu, for example, noted that People's War under high-tech conditions should focus on utilizing the cities' comprehensive, crisscross, and vertically-linked information network systems to carry out all kinds of organization work. China must rely on the cities to make the most of the strengths of high-tech personnel, to create a strong material force from national defense industries, to create a logistic support system for transport, and to create an unimpeded communications network. Che closed by reiterating the themes mentioned above regarding the mobilization of information resources. This includes the need to integrate peacetime production with preparedness for war, the need to enhance military-civilian compatibility and peacetime-wartime capabilities and compatibility, and the need to build an urban military reserve force.[219] The Science of Strategy book also underscored the fact that People's War corresponds not only to low-tech wars but also to high-tech ones. Arming the masses is to be carried out by organizing established units and deploying militia or reserve units. In addition, it was recommended by the Strategy authors to set up a mobilization database on the nationwide Internet and to use flexible and multiple means to continue to improve the scientific content and quality of war mobilization.[220]

One report during the 10th National People's Congress in 2003 further underscored the country's requirement for an information-age People's War. Delegates reportedly noted that "even under informationized conditions, China's military strategic guiding policy of active defense will still uphold the ideology of People's War."[221] Delegate Wang Wenhui noted that information resources "hidden among the masses" can

---

[217] Zhuang Yaoqing and Fang Hongxiang, "High Technology Goes into the 'Chinese Army Account'," Shanghai Jiefang Ribao, 10 September 2002, as translated and downloaded from the FBIS Web site on 13 September 2002. Shanghai Jiefang Ribao is the Internet version of the daily newspaper of the Shanghai Municipal CPC Committee. See www.jfdaily.com

[218] Zhang Qing, "Stepping up the Building of China's Scientific and Technological Mobilization Structure for National Defense," Zhongguo Guofang Bao , 23 January 2003 p. 4 as translated and downloaded from the FBIS Web site on 23 January 2003.

[219] Che Hu, "Grasp the New Strongholds of People's War," Zhongguo Guofang Bao, 13 January 2003 p. 3 as translated and downloaded from the FBIS Web site on 13 January 2003.

[220] Ge Zhenfeng

[221] Bai Ruixue, "Chinese Military Delegates Say War in the Information Age Still Requires the Support of People's War," Xinhua Asia-Pacific Service, 12 March 2003, as translated and downloaded from the FBIS Web site on 12 March 2003.

develop the strategic ideology of People's War in this era. By this he meant the IT talent possessed by many academicians and professors who have continued to join the militia and reserve forces. These forces interact with military units and provide brainpower in peacetime and direct participation in wartime. Another delegate, Hao Jingmin, stated that "when installing optical fiber communications cable, a certain capacity can be provided for wartime use by taking into account war readiness communications requirements and the extent of their wartime usage."[222] Delegates added that it will require an effective mobilization mechanism to convert information resources and war potential into combat power.[223] Thus the People's War concept should continue as a viable concept.

As regards the militia, subunits of the People's Armed Police Corps are undergoing intensive IW training, according to several reports over the past few years. In July of 1999 it was reported that North China held a specialized militia subunit exercise. It used an emergency communications subunit with digital communications means (satellite and wireless high-speed fax) to provide communications support to "combat troops." It also used a militia electronic countermeasure subunit to do electronic jamming and a militia computer network information subunit to monitor and attack an "enemy command network." It was reported that in the Shenyang military region there are now over one hundred militia high-tech subunits covering seventeen specialized fields such as modern communications, computers, automatic control, and electronic countermeasures.[224]

In order to stem the tide of Internet crime, China reportedly increased the size of its Internet police force in 2000 to some 300,000 personnel. These crime fighters are part of the Ministry of Public Security and, thus, may have jobs other than fighting crime (espionage, etc.). The Internet police are mainly responsible for analyzing information content flowing through local communication systems or the Internet, fighting computer viruses, cracking down on Internet crimes, and stopping the spread of "harmful information."[225]

On 12 January 2002 Jiefangjun Bao (Liberation Army Daily) reported on another militia exercise. This time it involved the XPCC Eighth Agricultural Division. The division reportedly established a high-tech militia branch at the Institute of Information Engineering at Shihezi University in the Xinjiang Uighur Region in 2001, and it built training bases, regional networks, and a central Web site. The division also developed a set of network assault software programs known as "Falcon" that was used in several online confrontation exercises involving the division.[226]

---

[222] Ibid.

[223] Ibid.

[224] "China's Reserve Defense Might Is Markedly High-Tech," Xinhua Hong Kong Service, 20 July 1999 as translated and downloaded from the FBIS Web site on 9 August 1999.

[225] "Inviting College Graduates with Special Skills to Work for Bureau," Ming Pao Web site, Hong Kong, 8 December 2000 obtained via e-mail from the internetcrimenews@infowar.com site.

[226] Guo Dongmin and Zheng Wenfa, "Innovations Make 'Implementation of Three Measures' No longer Difficult," Jiefangjun Bao (Liberation Army Daily), 12 January 2002 as translated and downloaded from the FBIS Web site on 12 January 2002.

Other Issues

The best and the brightest information-age authors of the Chinese military community wrote the articles used to support this chapter. An interesting question is: do other writers agree with these comments? The answer is, not necessarily. Since there appears to be both agreements and disagreements, it is likely that heated discussion on some issues is probably still underway.

In 2001 LTC Liu Aimin wrote that informationized war is the form that high-tech warfare takes "in the knowledge economy and the information age."[227] He discussed the characteristics of IW, listing the five most important characteristics as

- Informationized weapons systems with intelligent components
- Digitalization and the adding of a knowledge component to combat forces
- The addition of an all-dimensional and networked aspect to the information battlefield
- The movement of combat actions into the air and outer space, and their added dimension of precision
- The different forms that combat operations will take, resulting in more varied and more high-tech components
- And the integration of command systems, making them real-time.[228]

Liu also wrote that C4I systems are the center of gravity of enemy and friendly combat operations; and that informationized networks (highlighted by their integration capabilities, multiple links, and synchronization potential) will be the core of the informationized battlefield. He underscored that precision-guided weapons are the most obvious characteristic of high-tech warfare and, due to precision weapons' reliance on space-based systems, outer space has become the new main battlefield. Ground forces will serve as back-up forces. Liu concluded that the main forms of future combat operations would be electronic warfare, network warfare, computer virus warfare, noncontact operations, and space warfare.[229]

Less high profile but not necessarily less important authors tend to raise specific issues such as a potential IW war with Taiwan. For example, writer Wen T'ao covered many of the arguments listed above. He stated that China is coming closer to its goal of establishing "information control" by building and reinforcing its information infrastructure. This includes a (1) space-based early warning system (2) a satellite positioning system and (3) a command network system. This is necessary to continue to counter the preparations underway for IW by Taiwan, Wen believes. The General Staff Department of the PLA that is charged with IW responsibility has instructed combat units of the PLA to study and analyze Taiwan's IW tactics and to develop countermeasures in order to quickly seize the initiative. The author states that IW is warfare aimed at seizing

---

[227] [227] Liu Aimin, "The Characteristics of Informationized War," Zhongguo Junshi Kexue (China Military Science), 1 August 2001, pp. 69-72 as translated and downloaded from the FBIS Web site on 20 November 2003.
[228] Ibid.
[229] Ibid.

"information control" which reflects the "primary feature of high-tech warfare in an overall and fundamental perspective." To gain and maintain control means that information must be gathered in a timely manner, it must be accurately transmitted, and it must be effectively used.[230]

Wen also discussed China's plan to develop, through IW related institutes, key technologies that raise the standard of IW. In 1999 China reorganized the PLA Information Engineering Academy, the PLA Surveying Academy, and the PLA Electronic Technology Academy into the PLA Information Engineering University. The University has developed technologies marked by signal breakthroughs such as the "satellite-powered ground survey" technology and the "system for synchronic verification of gravity on long-range missiles' inertia-guidance systems." The PLA is reorganizing and integrating other technological forces as well.[231]

One area in which there still appears to be an ongoing debate is over the issue of information superiority. For example, General Dai's emphasis on information superiority was countered in another 2002 article in China Military Science. Author Wang Xingwang from the Academy of Military Science discussed some of the features of air, sea and electromagnetic domination, and concluded that electromagnetic domination is more appropriate than information domination.[232]

Wang stated that the target of control in all three operations is the use of the time-space continuum of the battlefield in question (air, sea or electromagnetic), each of which is somewhat independent of the other. Control and anti-control, use and anti-use, and contention and anti-contention are reflected in all operations to gain domination. This is a reflection of the dialectic aspect of Chinese thinking. What is controlled is a limited portion of battlefield space, not all the space in a war. Wang feels it is impossible to gain control of everything from strategies to campaigns to tactics. War has a visible and visible-invisible pattern due to the electromagnetic confrontation. This has accelerated the development of the electronic warfare unit.[233] Wang's emphasis on EW does, however, coincide with General Dai's emphasis on EW in his "integrated network-electronic warfare concept."

Wang argues that air, sea, and electromagnetic domination are "unitary" forms of domination (one dimensional) while information domination is "compound" domination (a composite of electromagnetic, network and other forms of unitary domination). He feels it is better to use the unitary elements side by side and not include the compound form of domination. He notes that information is an abstract that cannot be manipulated while information carriers can be controlled. Therefore information domination only refers to information carriers and not abstract information. As Wang notes, "the control

---

[230] Wen T'ao, "PLA Bent on Seizing 'Information Control'," Hong Kong Ching Pao, 1 June 2002, Number 299, pp. 44-46 as translated and downloaded from the FBIS web page on 5 June 2002.
[231] Ibid.
[232] Wang Xingwang, "Views on Theory of Dominant Operations—On Domination of Information and Traffic," Zhongguo Junshi Kexue (China Military Science), 20 June 2002, pp. 129-132, as translated and downloaded from the FBIS Web site on 4 December 2002.
[233] Ibid.

and use of the electromagnetic (EM) spectrum are the foci…when one controls the right of use of the EM spectrum space, one will seize the crucial point of operational information."[234] Wang's emphasis on "control" supports the focus on this issue by Shen and a few other Chinese theorists over the past five years.

Thus, from 2000-2003 the PLA made significant strides in its march to move from a mechanized to an information-based force with Chinese characteristics. They have even begun the development of their own "network-centric warfare" concept. As Wang Baocun noted

> Since the English language does not have the term "informationization," the US military cannot use the term "informationized warfare." The vast amount of expositions on "network-centric warfare" by the US military suggests that "network-centric warfare" is, in essence, a fusion of information warfare and precision engagement; it is very close to information-based warfare. It is not a type of warfare, much less the commonly known "cyberwarfare."[235]

Chapter Four, "China's IW-Stratagem Link" will underscore another Chinese specific characteristic of IW. The use of IW stratagems is rarely discussed in the West yet it is an area from which there is much to learn. The Chinese emphasis of the Serbian use of stratagems to offset coalition IW superiority mentioned in Chapter One was a case in point. Today, however, the Chinese military is also exploring how to use electrons as stratagems.

---

[234] Ibid.
[235] Wang Baocun, "The Future Warfare for Which the US Military is Making Preparations: Network-Centric Warfare," in Zhongguo Junshi Kexue (China Military Thought), 20 October 2002, pp. 133-143, as translated and downloaded from the FBIS Web site on 6 December 2003.

CHAPTER FOUR: CHINA'S IW-STRATEGY/STRATAGEM LINK

Introduction

Stratagems have historically been a key component of China's military culture. They are found in almost every aspect of Chinese military thought, to include command and control and information war. A Chinese <u>PLA Officer's Handbook</u> offered the best definitions of stratagem from a purely military viewpoint for purposes of this chapter. The handbook defined two related concepts: the science of military stratagem and military stratagem. The science of military stratagem is

> Both related to and distinguished from strategic science, campaign science, and tactical science. Strategic science, campaign science, and tactical science research problems related to either the full scope or specific aspects of war; however, the science of military stratagem researches problems related to the creation and application of stratagem that cut across all three of these sciences. Strategic science, campaign science, and tactical science research the general principles of war guidance; however, the science of military stratagem researches how to flexibly apply these general principles in war. If the former's research focuses on the "positive path," then the latter focuses on the "deceptive (or scheming) path"; if the former's research focuses on the "constant," then the latter focuses on the "variable..."[236]

Military stratagem was defined in the following way:

> Stratagem generally refers to scheming and military strategy (or tactics—<u>taolue</u>); the war planning (or scheme, plot—<u>mohua</u>) employed by the two opposing combatants to be used at different levels of military strategy, military campaign, and military tactics in order to obtain victory. Military stratagem is a product of the development of war, the concrete manifestation of human subjective actions upon material forces. It reflects the general principles of military struggles, possessing a corresponding stable nature and vigorous liveliness.[237]

There is mention of stratagems in many Chinese military articles. In a 2000 article in the Chinese journal <u>China Military Science</u>, authors Major General Niu Li, Colonel Li Jiangzou, and Major Xu Dehui (all of the Communications and Command Institute) defined IW stratagems as "schemes and methods devised and used by commanders and commanding bodies to seize and maintain information supremacy on the basis of using

---

[236] <u>Chinese People's Liberation Army Officer's Handbook</u>, Qingdao Publishing House, June 1991, p. 197. Translation support for the terms science of military stratagem and science of military stratagem was provided by Mr. John Tai, a George Washington University PhD candidate and consultant on Chinese affairs. Dr. Gary Bjorge of the Combat Studies Institute of Fort Leavenworth, Kansas made his <u>PLA Handbook</u> available for use.
[237] Ibid.

clever methods to prevail at a relatively small cost in IW."[238] The 1992 book Thirty-Six Stratagems offered another definition, noting that

> Yin and Yang are two complementary qualities in the universe and everything in the world is thought to belong to one or the other. Yin, the female element, is associated with the dark and hidden while Yang, the male element, is associated with light and openness. The ancient Chinese regarded ploys and stratagems often hatched and carried out in secrecy, to belong to the Yin. Yin in the Book of Changes is represented by the hexagram for earth which is composed of six lines, with each line broken into segments, resulting in two columns of six short lines, whose product is thirty-six.[239]

Chinese-English dictionaries referenced for this chapter used the words "plan, scheme, astuteness, resourcefulness, strategy, plot, and trickery" most often as an equivalent for stratagem. Thus there is some common understanding of a stratagem from a Chinese viewpoint. The word is understood to imply some measure of scheming, trickery, or deception.

The US Armed Forces does not recognize stratagem as part of its military philosophy. The US Department of Defense's Dictionary of Military Terms, Joint Publication (JP) 1-02, does not define the term. It does define strategy and tactics. The former is defined as "the art and science of developing and employing instruments of national power in a synchronized and integrated fashion to achieve theater, national, and/or multinational objectives." Tactics are defined as "the employment of units in combat. The ordered arrangement and maneuver of units in relation to each other and/or to the enemy in order to use their full potentialities."[240]

The term stratagem is not absent from the English language, of course. One US dictionary defined a stratagem as "a maneuver to deceive or outwit an enemy in war. It is a device for obtaining advantage; trick."[241] Strategy is defined as "the science and art of conducting a military campaign on a broad scale: distinguished from tactics. The use of stratagem or artifice, as in business or politics. A plan or technique for achieving some end."[242] Tactics are defined as "the science and art of military and naval evolutions; especially, the art of handling troops in the presence of the enemy or for immediate objectives; distinguished from strategy. Any maneuvering or adroit management to gain an objective."[243] This indicates that the US understanding of the term also is related to trickery and deception.

---

[238] Niu Li, Li Jiangzhou, and Xu Dehui, "Planning and Application of Strategies of Information Operations in High-Tech Local War," Zhongguo Junshi Kexue (China Military Science), Number 4 2000, pp. 115-122 as translated and downloaded from the FBIS Web site on 9 November 2000
[239] Koh Kok Kiang, and Liu Yi (translators), Secret Art of War: Thirty-Six Stratagems, 1992, Asiapac Books, Singapore, Forward.
[240] See http://www.dtic.mil/doctrine/jel/doddict/, as amended through 17 December 2003.
[241] Funk and Wagnalls Standard College Dictionary, Harcourt, Brace, and World, 1968, p. 1323.
[242] Ibid.
[243] Ibid., p. 1363.

Still, it is difficult to capture the overall essence of a stratagem and what it implies to Chinese theorists who use the term. Dr. William Whitson, an American who has studied the Chinese for many years, offered an interpretation of a stratagem from what might be termed an overarching perspective of a Chinese specialist with years of experience in the field of military studies:

> I have never seen a Western term that adequately expresses what it means. Westerners don't understand the essence of the concept. They seek oversimplified words like 'deception' or 'disinformation.' The practitioner of mou lue zhan starts from the premise that he is engaged not in destroying the enemy physically but in confusing him mentally, hopefully so confusing the enemy that he will become paralyzed. The idea is based on a deeper philosophical idea that any situation is not objectively real. It is instead a projection of many perceptions, especially the perception of leaders. So the focus of mou lue zhan is an enemy leader's perception…it might be translated as 'attitude warfare' or 'perception warfare.' In effect, military strategy itself and the deployment of troops are made subordinate to the overarching stratagem of creating the enemy's perception. Westerner's don't understand it because they are taught to believe that victory comes to those with things that make the loudest noise and are the most destructive. To the mou lue warrior, such a viewpoint is childish and wasteful.[244]

Dr. Deborah Porter is a Chinese language specialist at the University of Washington. She added a supporting yet slightly different interpretation of the term. In the ancient dictionary Erya, Dr. Porter writes, mou is defined as "heart." An annotator of the definition commented that "mou" is using the heart to think (in a calculating way). Mou is also defined as the type of thought that assesses the difficulty or easiness of some action. Sixteen synonyms of the term were listed in the Erya dictionary, including to plan, to delimit, to surprise, to search, to investigate, to visit, and to observe (for the purpose of calculation).[245] In the section on "Shi Yan" (explanations of verbal expressions) where mou is defined by itself, the same definition of "relying on the heart to think" is listed but with more commentary: "the heart is [like] the finest of thread; [its ability] to recognize/discern the minutest [details] ensure that there is no object that cannot be penetrated; the heart is the residence of cognition."[246]

The Chinese word zhan, Dr. Porter adds, was usually used in the context of warfare and had an ancient meaning more to do with the emotion/sensation of fear. In a military context, an understanding of the objective would be how fear is manipulated, created, and taken advantage of—often in tandem with an element of "surprise" in a battle context. It is also understood as a word for trembling, such as a shaking movement as a response to fear.[247]

---

[244] E-mail correspondence with Dr. William W. Whitson, 13 April 2004. Dr. Whitson is the author of The Chinese High Command, a comprehensive study of China's military elite. He served as a military attaché to Taiwan and Hong Kong, and received his PhD from the Fletcher School of Law and Diplomacy.
[245] Erya, Beijing: Zhonghua Shuju, 1982, Vol. 1, p. 19a. Footnotes based on e-mail correspondence with Dr. Deborah Porter, University of Washington, 18 April 2004.
[246] Ibid., p. 52b.
[247] Ibid., p. 73a.

The term lue is not as ancient as the other two, at least as is recorded in paleographic and dictionary sources, according to Dr. Porter. The initial sense of the term was agricultural. The semantic sense of the term may have evolved to include the sense of plot or ploy. It has nothing to do with battle. The word lue in mou lue zhan refers to the plan/plot and calculations/observations conducted with the object of manipulating (psychologically) opponents' emotions, especially those associated with fear, Dr. Porter concludes.[248] Thus, with this complicated etymology, it is not surprising that "stratagem" is a concept not entirely understood by Western audiences.

The Chinese are integrating stratagems into their information-age thinking at many levels. For example, the book Command Decision-Making and Stratagem, published in 1999, took a historical look at China's tradition of using stratagems. Author Zian Ruyi noted that "historical wars needed stratagems and future high-tech wars also need stratagems even more. We must …make them more scientific and modern."[249] Jia Fengshan, writing in Jiefangjun Bao (Liberation Army Daily) in 2003, noted that science and technology boost traditional stratagems to a new level. They can be derived from and applied to not only the human brain but also high-tech means. Jia noted that "some military experts believe that the 'differences in stratagems' lie in the 'differences in technologies' under high-tech conditions" and that integrating high-tech with stratagems is going to be an inevitable trend in the future.[250]

The term is often used with other concepts. When discussing the term asymmetry, for example, one Chinese theorist chose to mix the term stratagem with the term tactics. Kang Hengzhen, writing in China Military Science in 2002, noted that "12 crafty tactics" demonstrate the abnormal logic that defines asymmetry. Further, asymmetric operations are no longer constrained spatially due to the advent of high-tech (which has information technology as its core). Traditional fighting space has changed. Now ground forces must be prepared to consider the effect of satellites that spy on their every move as well as the opponent's ground forces. It is necessary to consider the stratagems that fool these satellites.[251]

These constant references to stratagems indicate that they play a key role whether directly or indirectly in the development of Chinese IW theory and practice. This chapter explains how China uses stratagems in conjunction with IW. First, China is studying how to deceive and manipulate the decision-making capability of commanders through the integration of IW and stratagems. Second, the Chinese military is studying how stratagems and high-tech equipment work together. For example, Chinese planners are learning how to gather reconnaissance data (obtained from satellites, sensors, etc.) from

---

[248] E-mail exchange with Dr. Porter, 18 April 2004.
[249] Zian Ruyi, Command Decision-Making and Stratagem, Kunlun Publishing House, Beijing 1999, pp. 4-5, 76-87, 92-97 as translated and downloaded from the FBIS Web site on 24 April, 2003.
[250] Jia Fengshan, "Strategists Embrace High-Tech," Jiefangjun Bao (Liberation Army Daily), 9 April 2003 (Internet version), as translated and downloaded from the FBIS Web site on 10 April 2003.
[251] Kang Hengzhen, "The Origin and Development of Asymmetric Strategy," Zhongguo Junshi Kexue (China Military Science), Number 3, 2002, pp. 70-76 as translated and downloaded from the FBIS Web site on 6 March 2003.

the battlefield, compare that data with other data stored in computers, and generate computer stratagems for action (similar to the US courses of action) based on this comparison. Third, based on a network analysis highlighting its critical aspects, attack stratagems are tailored to the different characteristics of the network under consideration. And finally, there is the implication that electron packets are capable of being used as stratagems against networks much as forces were used on a battlefield in the past.

The term stratagem is used often by the PLA, and it is a term that Western audiences must come to understand. It utilizes perception management techniques to fool or paralyze enemy forces. Understanding how the PLA interprets the terms also allows better contextual and philosophical understanding by Westerners of Chinese military writings. This chapter explores China's use of both IW strategies and stratagems.

Integrating High-Tech Weaponry with Stratagems

The topic of developing information warfare strategies and tactics has taken center stage as a key discussion point over the past few years. Even former Chinese President Jiang Zemin underscored the strategic task of "developing the strategies and tactics of People's War in the context of high technology" in his report to the 16th CPC National Congress.

Major General Dai Qingmin, director of the PLA's Communication Department of the General Staff (responsible for IW/IO), is one Chinese thinker who has done as Jiang directed. He wrote in the Number 4, 2000 issue of <u>China Military Science</u> that

> …new technologies are likely to find material expression in informationalized arms and equipment which will, together with information systems, sound, light, electronics, magnetism, heat, and so on, turn into a carrier of strategies.[252]

Dai's comments imply that China may intend to use electrons as they once used forces. That is, electrons might be used to fulfill the stratagems "kill with a borrowed sword" and "exhaust the enemy at the gate and attack him at your ease." Electrons might, for example, help destroy another country's information infrastructure or overcome deficiencies in technology just as forces did in the past. A comparable equivalent to this theoretical development in military art would be Russia creating a virtual operational maneuver group (OMG) of electron forces to attack inside a country, maneuvering electrons as forces were once manipulated.

General Dai's article is an important benchmark in PLA military philosophy. First, as the prior commander of the PLA's Information Warfare Center in Wuhan, General Dai is a very credible and responsible figure, giving his ideas the stamp of official thinking. Second, in the article quoted above, General Dai broke with tradition and advocated an active offensive to gain the initiative and seize information superiority by attacking first. This offensive emphasis contradicts China's military strategy of active

---

[252] Dai Qingmin, "Innovating and Developing Views on Information Operations," <u>Zhongguo Junshi Kexue (China Military Science)</u>, Number 4 2000, pp. 72-77 as translated and downloaded from the FBIS Web site on 9 November 2000.

defense and indicates new missions for IW forces. Finally, he noted that integrated and joint IO, two subjects rarely discussed by Chinese specialists, gives more scope and purpose to a People's War. Dai's support of stratagem-based activities and the writings of other Chinese analysts on the subject should be closely followed by Western analysts.

Another important article in <u>China Military Science</u> that should be reviewed is "Planning and Application of Strategies of Information Operations in High-Tech Local Wars." Authors Major General Niu Li (a professor), Colonel Li Jiangzhou (an associate professor), and Major Xu Dehui (a lecturer) at the Communications and Command Institute offered several ways in which stratagems could be applied in the information age.[253]

The authors defined information warfare stratagems as "schemes and methods devised and used by commanders and commanding bodies to seize and maintain information supremacy on the basis of using clever methods to prevail at a relatively small cost in information warfare."[254] According to Niu, Li, and Xu, Orientals and Occidentals view the combination of stratagems and technology in different ways. This is because their military and social cultures, not to mention their economic prosperity, have evolved in different ways which results in different thought processes. The authors noted:

> Traditionally, Oriental people emphasize stratagems, and Occidental people emphasize technology…Occidental soldiers would seek technological means when encountering a difficulty, while Oriental soldiers would seek to use stratagems to make up for technological deficiencies without changing the technological conditions. An Oriental soldier's traditional way of thinking is not conducive to technological development, but can still serve as an effective way of seeking survival in a situation of danger.[255]

There is certainly a Western proclivity to look for technological fixes that has long been recognized and critiqued by analysts. A simple check on when the latest US article was written on IW stratagems would most likely turn up empty. Western audiences have underappreciated the less recognized Oriental fix on strategies and perhaps their importance in general. A proper mix of the two is required, it would seem, to ensure that all sides of a situation are properly assessed.

Authors Niu, Li, and Xu believe that stratagems can help China make up for its deficiencies in high-technology based weaponry. Stratagems are not developed in isolation but by combining human qualitative thinking with computer-assisted quantitative calculations. There are reports of Chinese efforts to use computers to generate military stratagems as a battle unfolds in field exercises. In such scenarios, the operations department of a field unit would collect information from sensors, satellites, and other reconnaissance assets, and enter the data into a computer. The computer would generate stratagems from this input for a Chinese commander's consideration. That is,

---

[253] Niu Li, Li Jiangzhou, and Xu Dehui.
[254] Ibid.
[255] Ibid.

current battlefield information is compared with established models stored in computers, and from this stratagems are generated. US operations personnel, on the other hand, generate courses of action for their commander's consideration. This is usually done by a combination of map and terrain analysis and knowledge of enemy locations.

The PLA Science and Technology University reportedly has developed an auxiliary decision-making system for military operations research. This may be the machine that produces these calculations. The system improves the PLA's simulated operations capability. It should enhance their combat prognosis capability and ability to grasp tactical situations. This is particularly helpful when considering operational factors such as troop strength, firepower, and sea/air control capabilities, and when performing force-on-force exercises on the network.[256]

The Chinese believe that the models stored in computers will standardize responses to the huge number of contingencies and uncertainties on the battlefield. Computers and the human brain interact to develop IW stratagems under these circumstances. As these authors put it, it is necessary to "let stratagems be integrated into the genes of high technology."[257]

One goal of the use of stratagems is to cause enemy commanders to make mistakes by influencing their cognitive elements and system of beliefs. The idea is to force enemy commanders to develop decisions in the direction set by the Chinese side.[258] Another idea is to fool the high-tech systems, such as sensors and satellites, with fake troop movements or locations. In this way enemy commanders are shown a false picture of what is developing which influences the decisions they eventually make.

LTC Liu Aimin, a staff officer in a General Staff Department of the PLA, added to this idea. He wrote that deception warfare is rising quietly on virtual battlefields. By this he means the insertion of simulated information into an enemy's command and control system. This could cause an enemy to mistake what is false for what is true, or it could throw an enemy command and control scheme into chaos. Liu concluded that "virtual reality information network deception will become an important combat measure on the future virtual battlefield."[259]

Cybernetics, information theory, systems theory and futurology, and decision-making systems and theories assist this effort. Chinese theorists use these tools to search for critical points and weak spots in an enemy's system, and then they find ways to paralyze the system. To make this work, junctures and areas of interaction between technology and stratagems must be identified. Stratagems must be devised to be compatible with the characteristics of different networks, and they must be used by a

---

[256] China News Agency, http://www.chinanews.com.cn/n/2003-04-07/26/291859.html, 7 April 2003.
[257] Li Nui, Li Jiangzhou, and Xu Dehui.
[258] Ibid.
[259] Liu Aimin, "The Characteristics of Informationized War," Zhongguo Junshi Kexue (China Military Science), 1 August 2001, pp. 69-72 as translated and downloaded from the FBIS Web site on 20 November 2003.

system capable of ensuring information acquisition, transmission, and processing. They must control the entire process in a targeted manner that requires an understanding of how an information contest develops in different stages and time periods. Here, Chinese authors place emphasis on attacking first. This is yet another indication that in the information age an active offense may be more important than an active defense.[260]

In the acquisition or preparation phase, stratagems must interfere with, damage or destroy listening and antilistening measures, camouflage and anticamouflage devices, reconnaissance and antireconnaissance measures, and stealth and antistealth measures among other items. Stratagems may be included in information flows to sever channels of communication while keeping friendly flows of information secure. Some of the methods of influencing information flows are to carry out interference and anti-interference efforts, deciphering and antideciphering efforts, and destruction and antidestruction efforts. Finally, the processing phase requires stratagems that, in addition to the transmission task, include misleading and antimisleading efforts targeting the enemy's information processing system to cause the enemy to make decision-making errors.[261]

The basic goal of stratagems is to intimidate, use perception management, and create fictitious objects (such as fake networks and equipment in an information system) as part of a deception plan whose intent is to hide "true reality." The intellectual battle is now more important than contests in bravery, the authors note, and wide-ranging knowledge and superior wisdom, boldness, and scheming ability are required.[262]

A stratagem can be as simple as misleading the enemy by pretending to follow his wishes. If one knows the enemy's intentions, the enemy can be led into a trap.

A contest in information warfare stratagem is usually conducted in a non-contact manner, and contains efforts to create cognitive errors on the part of the enemy and to influence the contents, process, and direction of thinking on the part of the enemy's commanders and relevant personnel for information warfare; the purpose is to make enemy commanders make wrong decisions or even stop fighting, so as to achieve the objectives of information warfare without fighting.[263]

Of course, the actual effectiveness of this strategy would need to be evaluated based on the enemy's perceived awareness of the strategy's intent and subsequent response. Finally, Niu, Li, and Xu offered ten specific stratagems (which read more like methods) that can be applied to IW. These stratagems include:

(1) **Thought-Directing**—Direct others' thinking in the wrong decision by attacking cognitive and belief systems and force commanders to make errors. Use schemes with

---

[260] Li Nui, Li Jiangzhou, and Xu Dehui. The Chinese use "thought directing" in this article in the way a US analyst would use perception management.
[261] Ibid.
[262] Ibid.
[263] Ibid.

regard to enemy doubts and exploit information relays between enemy units and departments.

(2) **Intimidation through Momentum-Building**—Generate heavy psychological pressure via intimidation by signaling inevitable victory, concentrating forces, and coordinating information networks. This is to be achieved by creating a situation favorable to China and unfavorable to the enemy. Intimidation is to be achieved via momentum building, achieved by enhancing one's own position, situation, and posture while blocking the flow of information to the enemy.

(3) **Information-based Capability Demonstrations**—Intimidate by demonstrating capabilities, an action that should not appear to be intentional. The right time, occasion, and modality must be chosen to make information believable to the enemy. At the same time, a unit's true strength should not be revealed, and one should be unpredictable, using both true and false information.

(4) **Prevailing over the Enemy with Extraordinary Means**—Adopt active and effective measures to generate surprise, and use decisive technical equipment and means of information warfare. Develop and hide information warfare "killer weapons."

(5) **Using Fictitious Objects to Hide the True Picture**—Hide true reality by creating a fictitious reality. Simulate combat forces using high-tech means, to include the creation of nonexistent objects (such as fictitious networks and information system, as well as fictitious strategic and operational objectives).

(6) **All-Encompassing Deception**—Apply deceptive schemes simultaneously or consecutively according to strategic or operational intentions. Actions taken should be coordinated and corroborated with one another to ensure the enemy will have no suspicion.

(7) **Prevailing over the Enemy with All-round Strength**—Use all means of information warfare to maintain supremacy. Electronic soft attacks (reconnaissance satellite systems, etc.), hard attacks (informationized precision-guidance weapons, strategic bombings), and C3I battlefield control and management must all be present.

(8) **Going with the Flow**—Mislead the enemy by pretending to follow his wishes. Pretend to "go with the flow" by exploiting one's knowledge of an enemy's intentions and the detection of enemy moves in order to lead the enemy into a trap.

(9) **Releasing "Viruses" to Muddy the Flows**—Release viruses to contaminate information flows. Using viruses, the authors note, is an important combat operation. A virus attack is "a technical act, which will have to be based on the use of stratagems in order to play an important role in IW." Stratagems should create a favorable time for releasing viruses. It is important not only to seize opportunities but also to create opportunities, and to "attack first." [This idea of preemption was also noted in Chapter Three.]

(10) **Controlling the Time Element**—Control of the time element is crucial. Conducting information "inducement," "deception," concealment," and "containment" operations will help achieve the desired amount of control. [264]

In conclusion, the authors noted that "there are many ways of seizing information supremacy and the initiative in IW, and the use of stratagems is one of the most efficient ways." The goal of the use of stratagems to Niu, Li, and Xu is to force an opponent to refrain from deciding to launch information attacks in order to achieve objectives without direct fighting. The point of these strategies is to create cognitive errors in the enemy; to influence the contents, process, and direction of thinking on the part of enemy commanders; and to create a multidimensional threat with which the enemy must contend.[265]

Focus on Science and Technology, Not Just Strategy

China's focus on stratagems is a cultural and historical fact. However, some key Chinese theorists recently questioned whether there it too extensive a reliance on stratagems. If stratagems are being stressed at the expense of technology, then perhaps a weakness has emerged in Chinese military thought that must be corrected. As a result some theorists are trying to better harmonize an integration of high-tech with stratagems.

One of the most prominent Chinese theorists to challenge the stratagem-centered approach is Major General Li Bingyan, Senior Editor of the Liberation Army Daily (Jiefangjun Bao). More importantly he is the author of several works on stratagems and is considered a Chinese expert in the field of strategy. In 2002 Li wrote in support of placing more effort on scientific innovation. He also noted that, traditionally, Easterners put more emphasis on strategy, and Westerners put more emphasis on technology.[266]

Li writes that Western military power cultures see coordination and struggle as mutually incompatible, whereas Chinese culture emphasizes coordination within competition to seek a point of equilibrium between the interests of the two aspects. Chinese strategists pursue a battle of wits instead of relying on force. As a result, victory beyond the battlefield is a reflection of "big system ideology" in Chinese military

---

[264] Ibid.

[265] Ibid.

[266] Li Bingyan, "Emphasis on Strategy: Demonstrating the Culture of Eastern Military Studies," Zhongguo Junshi Kexue (China Military Science), 20 October 2002, pp. 80-85 as translated and downloaded from the FBIS Web site on 9 January 2003. Li notes that when Westerners consider a problem, they stress "is it a matter of this or of that?" which is helpful in scientific research. Easterners stress "what is this like, and what is that like?" which is helpful in reaching a profound understanding of societal relationships. As a result, research in China into the "cultural genes and methodologies of Chinese military science and strategy" takes into consideration the Yin and Yang (negative and positive), which is said to have originated in the Book of Changes, or I Ching, and the five-elements (water, fire, metal, wood, and earth) theory. In ancient times, odd- and even-numbered changes referred to changes in battle formations, while true and false changes referred to deception methods to set up an enemy for an attack. Each of China's stratagems is based on this doctrine of changes according to Li. The "Yin-Yang and five-elements theory" addresses mutual attraction and the achievement of overall equilibrium and balance through system coordination in addition to the elimination of contradictions.

strategy. All of these elements must remain a part of Chinese military strategy, but another element must be established—the emphasis not only on trickery and stratagems but on technology. Li notes:

> While we are the inheritors of our own outstanding cultural tradition, we should be boldly collecting cultural genes from Western military science and its emphasis on technology. We should make traditional strategy merge with modern science and technology and scientific methods, so as to restore the original intent of 'Sun Tzu strategy.'[267]

In view of Li's criticism of his system, should Western theorists spend more time on thinking in terms of strategy and the stratagems of warfare? Isn't it a known fact that Western armies already spend too much time and focus on technology to answer and fix every problem? Wasn't a focused reliance on technology at the expense of stratagems part of the reason that NATO's air forces did not hit targets as well as expected during the fight for Kosovo?[268] The answer to all of these questions is obvious and indicates that, indeed, the US should spend more time on developing stratagems.

Chinese authors Niu, Li, and Xu, mentioned above, also touched on the subject of the integration of stratagems and technology. They noted that information acquisition and processing capacities, and a system's overall anti-interference and survival capacities, will greatly affect the use of information warfare stratagems.[269] Today, China is in an inferior position in regard to other developing countries and their technological capabilities, although their capabilities are quickly rising. Therefore, it may be necessary to defeat superior equipment with inferior equipment until this ratio can be improved. To do this will require a combination of technology and stratagems in order to allow the "all rounded superior" to defeat those superior in equipment only.

Chinese experts recognize that every piece of equipment has vulnerabilities (even high-technology equipment) and that methods must be developed to attack these vulnerabilities. Examples include subjecting night vision devices to intense light or exploiting existing vulnerabilities, such as the Abrams tank's vulnerability to sand that was exposed during Desert Storm. Likewise, using operational security measures as the Serbs did in Kosovo (not turning on systems, placing mockups where equipment once was located, positioning tanks near other heat sources in villages, etc.) limited the combat effectiveness of high-tech NATO weapons. The most important point is that *man must create these conditions*, according to the Chinese. He must take advantage of enemy errors or force them to happen since man cannot entrust a nation's destiny only to the errors that the enemy makes. That is why Chinese scientists and theorists must study "methods of operation and performance parameters" in depth.[270]

---

[267] Ibid.

[268] For further discussion of this issue, see Timothy L. Thomas, "Kosovo and the Current Myth of Information Superiority," Parameters, Spring 2000, pp. 13-29.

[269] Niu, Li , and Xu.

[270] Information Warfare.

All these offensive and defensive methods of operation must be based on a thorough understanding of the operational and technical performance of the enemy's and our own weapons and equipment…we must have a thorough knowledge of the enemy's situation, our own situation, and the situation in the battleground….we should study, in depth, the weapons and equipment of our enemy in the operation, identify their Achilles' heel, and work out ways to overpower them.[271]

General Dai on IW Strategies

In the same issue that <u>China Military Science</u> published Niu, Li, and Xu's article, it also published Major General Dai's article on "Innovating and Developing Views on Information Operations," mentioned earlier in this chapter. Dai defined an information operation as "a series of operations with an information environment as the basic battlefield condition, with military information and an information system as the direct operational target, and with electronic warfare and a computer network war as the principal form."[272] Since these operations are a confrontation of forces and arms as well as a trial of strength focusing on knowledge and strategies, Dai recommended a "focus on strategies."

Dai noted that scientific and technological developments have given strategies a new playing field. A strategy may carry different contents under different technological conditions. Thus, there is room for traditional strategies, but also room for mapping out new strategies using new technological means. Options include new information-confrontation strategies.[273] Overall a good strategy may

> Serve as a type of invisible fighting capacity; may make up inadequate material conditions to a certain extent; may narrow a technological or equipment gap between an army and its enemy; and may make up a shortage of information fighting forces or poor information operational means.[274]

Some specific strategies include:

- Jamming or sabotaging an enemy's information or information system
- Sabotaging an enemy's overall information operational structure
- Weakening an enemy's information fighting capacity
- Dispersing enemy forces, arms, and fire while concentrating one's own forces, arms, and fire
- Confusing or diverting an enemy and creating an excellent combat opportunity for oneself
- Diverting an enemy's reconnaissance attempt and making sufficient preparations for itself

---

[271] Ibid.
[272] Dai, "Innovating and Developing Views on Information Operations."
[273] Ibid.
[274] Ibid.

- Giving an enemy a false impression and launching a surprise information attack on an enemy at the same time
- Blinding or deafening an enemy with all sorts of false impressions
- Confusing an enemy's mind or disrupting an enemy's thinking
- Making an enemy believe what is true is false and what is false is true
- And making an enemy come up with a wrong judgment or take a wrong action.[275]

Dai also emphasized that future operations must be integrated, this time meaning to include the use of military and civilian information fighting forces. Information systems are offering more modes for people to take part in IO and offer people a chance to serve as a major auxiliary information fighting force in a future information war.[276]

According to Dai the attainment of information superiority [General Dai used the term information superiority thirty-two times in this article and the term information control, which Dr. Shen used so often, eleven times] is crucial to the utilization of these strategies in a People's War. This will require several steps. First, General Dai noted that professional forces [probably the PLA] would obtain, transmit, and process war information, and jam or sabotage enemy information or information systems. Nonprofessional forces [possibly the reserves] would protect specific targets and injure the effective fighting strength of the enemy. Second, electronic-warfare means (designed to sabotage information gathering and transmission) should be integrated with network-warfare means (designed to sabotage information processing and utilization). Third "soft and hard"[277] forces and offensive and defensive operations should be used. Offensive operations consist of electronic, network, and other units that are used to destroy enemy electronic systems. Defensive operations consist of telecommunications, technical reconnaissance, radar, and other units. The fourth and final step is the employment of an all-dimensional operation that includes integrated and joint operations of ground, sea, air, and space activities.[278]

General Dai remarked that compared to traditional air, ground, and naval operations, to actively contend with an enemy for information superiority, the Chinese need to "establish such a view for information operations as 'active offense.'" The subsequent China White Paper that stressed China's adherence to an active defense posture contradicts this viewpoint. However, Dai's position does support Shen's proposition that China needed an "offensive-based defense," and Dai added that for defense to be positive it must be an "active offensive defense." A negative information defense is one that is passive. This word game may be designed to keep the "information active offense" in line with the White Paper. Dai recommended the active model of

---

[275] Ibid.

[276] Ibid.

[277] Ibid. "Soft" means of employment (temporary sabotage or deception) refer to electronic jamming, computer-virus attacks, network infiltration, carbonized-fiber bombs, virtual reality attacks, psychological attacks and so on. "Hard" means of employment (permanent sabotage, weakening the overall fighting capacity of an enemy) include conventional arms, sabotage attacks with forces, attacks with electromagnetic pulses, attacks with arms carrying direction finders, and so on.

[278] Ibid.

resistance used in Kosovo by Serbian forces against the coalition instead of the passive model of resistance used by Iraq during the 1991 Gulf War.

Dai added that stratagems can be used to formulate a strategy before launching or fighting a war, to serve as a sharp sword that sabotages and weakens a superior enemy while protecting or enhancing its own fighting capacity, to serve as a type of invisible fighting capacity, and to evade combat with a stronger enemy.[279] Dai stated that new developments had created challenges to some traditional strategies while promoting excellent conditions for others. He did not specify which strategies he had in mind. However, if defeating strong forces with weak forces in future IW is a goal that stratagems can support or supplement, then stratagems may be one of China's asymmetric means to combat US high technology.[280] In this sense, stratagems would be one of the "magic weapons" that the Chinese are always stressing.

In summary, the August 2000 article by General Dai in China Military Science may represent one of the most important IW articles written in China in the past three years. These thoughts included his reference to electronics as a potential carrier of strategies; the requirement for an active offense in IW; and the need in China for an integrated network-electronic warfare (INEW) concept. Either the INEW concept or the concept of informationized weapons is a close equivalent to the US "network centric warfare" concept. The INEW thoughts were later reflected in China's 2002 White Paper.

Further Thoughts on Stratagems

As mentioned above, Jia Fengshan wrote in 2003 that there is a "growing incorporation between science and technology on the one hand and traditional military stratagems on the other." He continued that "this trend will not only provide war conductors with new material means by which to work out their strategies, but also make the elevation of the traditional stratagems to a brand new level possible."[281] Information technologies such as computers, man-made satellites, and optical fiber communications have created more room for commanders to work out stratagems.[282] Military strategists working on stratagems must take high-tech factors into account, as it could lead to a boost in fighting capacity. Technical means possess the ability to take the enemy by surprise. Due to the ever-increasing application and integration of high-tech with stratagems commanders must change "their way of thinking, renew their knowledge, and improve their capability to master automatic command systems."[283]

In a February 2002 issue of China Military Science author Kang Hengzhen, a Senior Colonel and research fellow at General Staff Headquarters, discussed asymmetry. He defined it as "abnormal logic bringing together two sides that are pitted one against the other. It radiates the dialectic with 12 crafty tactics."[284] Asymmetrical thinking

---

[279] Ibid.
[280] Ibid.
[281] Jia Fengshan, "Strategists Embrace High-Tech."
[282] Ibid.
[283] Ibid.
[284] Kang Hengzhen.

includes understanding the nature and attributes of the other party, plus their needs and capabilities. This thinking is "hidden in China's active defense, and it has become a complete system of theories about preparing for war, strategic defense, strategic counterattack and offense, and so on."[285] High technology with information technology as the core has broken the spatial restraints that confined asymmetrical operations in the past, according to Kang. Characteristics of asymmetrical operations are their uncertain objectives, time of use, location, and means of employment. Finally, the author noted that those who can fight asymmetrical wars are those with superior scientific-technological strength and those with superior art of command.[286]

Another way that the information age (not mentioned in Dai's article except tangentially, when he noted that information systems and electronics could be carriers of strategies) might affect China's selection of a form of warfare is whether China can find ways to apply electrons to the thirty-six stratagems of war. Some three hundred years ago, an unknown scholar decided to collect all of China's thirty-six stratagems and write them down. His work was called The Secret Art of War: The 36 Stratagems. The work emphasized deception as a military art that can achieve military objectives. In the information age, which is characterized by anonymous attacks and uncertainty (for example, virus attacks or the existence of backdoors in programs, making anyone feel vulnerable), the stratagems might acquire an electronic identity that is used to fool or deceive. It should be easier to deceive or inflict perception management injuries ("guidance injuries" according to some translations of Chinese writings) as a result. Thus, the information age is developing into the age of anonymous persuaders and manipulators.

Some argue that in today's high-tech world, these ancient stratagems are no longer applicable. However, a look at just the first five stratagems demonstrates that this is not the case. Stratagem One is "fool the emperor to cross the sea." This means that in order to lower an enemy's guard you must act in the open while hiding your true intentions under the guise of common, daily activities. The IW application would be to use regular e-mail services or business links over the Internet to mask the insertion of malicious code or viruses. Stratagem Two is "Besiege Wei to rescue Zhao." This means that when the enemy is too strong to attack directly, then attack something he holds dear. The IW application is that if you can't hit someone with nuclear weapons due to the catastrophic effects on your own country, then attack the servers and nets responsible for Western financial, power, political and other systems stability with electrons. Stratagem Three is "Kill with a borrowed sword." This means that when you do not have the means to attack your enemy directly, then attack using the strength of another. The IW application is simple—send your viruses or malicious code through a surrogate or another country. Stratagem Four is "Await the exhausted enemy at your ease." This means that it is an advantage to choose the time and place for battle. Encourage your enemy to expend his energy in futile quests while you conserve your strength. When he is exhausted and confused, you attack with energy and purpose. The IW application here is to use the People's War theory to send out multiple attacks while saving the significant attack for

---

[285] Ibid.
[286] Ibid.

the time when all of the West's computer emergency response teams (CERT) are engaged. Finally Stratagem Five is "Loot a burning house." This means that when a country is beset by internal conflicts, then it will be unable to deal with an outside threat. The IW application is to put hackers inside the West (under the guise of a student or business) and attack from the inside. While chaos reigns, steal from information resource bases.

Interestingly enough, in Chapter Two it was noted by Dr. Shen that "people have come up with 36 ways to disrupt the Internet and 36 ways to defend against such disruption." Is it possible that Shen was referring to the thirty-six stratagems of war? Most Chinese will probably think of the thirty-six stratagems since this magic number is a classic ingredient of Chinese numerology, which remains a major part of modern Chinese rhetoric.

Finally, as mentioned earlier, information technology is the core and foundation of the military revolution according to many Chinese military theorists. Invisible forces must be considered in calculating the correlation of forces today. These forces include computing capabilities, to include capacity, communications capacity/volume, system reliability, and the increasing competency and ability of reconnaissance systems to foresee situations.[287] Each of these elements could be victims of a manipulation stratagem and consequently affect the perception of the user of the system in question. That is, an information strategy can be employed against adversaries by toying with a side's information infrastructure's capacity, capabilities, and reliability, all of which are crucial elements in maintaining infrastructure stability. Since information technology possesses global reach, speed of light transmission due to the Internet, and comprehensive integration, the use of stratagems against information infrastructures can have immediate and perhaps long-lasting consequences.

Psychological Manipulation

In its essence, a stratagem is about out-thinking the opponent, forcing the enemy to believe something that is not true. The idea is to manipulate an opponent into a decision or into a movement that is advantageous to friendly forces. Thus stratagems have a significant psychological aspect. Knowledge war also includes the development of superior strategies based on superior knowledge.

Future war may be characterized by chessboard type competition. High-tech knowledge embedded into the circuitry of weaponry will be "directed by master's degree holders, commanded by university students, and conducted by experts." In addition the speed of turning knowledge into weapons will increase as will network competence, automation and real-time systems of early warning, reconnaissance, control and guidance, and attack. This will enable weapons to automatically conduct analysis, and differentiate and identify targets. People and weaponry that are more technologically competent will enable military systems to replace "quantity and scale" with "quality and

---

[287] Hai Lung and Chang Feng, "Chinese Military Studies Information Warfare," Kuang Chiao Ching, Number 280, 16 January 1996, pp. 22-23 as translated in FBIS-CHI-96-035, 21 February 1996, pp. 33-34.

effectiveness."[288] Such advantages will give friendly forces a significant psychological advantage as well.

In the next chapter a closer look at China's understanding of psychological operations is offered. The emphasis the Chinese put on this subject is much more intense than that in Western countries most likely because it reflects the roots of Chinese military culture that emphasize "winning without fighting."

---

[288] Jia Xi and Shi Hongju, "Analysis on Key Elements of Knowledge Warfare," Jiefangjun Bao (Liberation Army Daily) (Internet Version-WWW), 18 September 2000 as translated and downloaded from the FBIS Web site on 18 September 2000.

CHAPTER FIVE: CHINESE STRATEGIC PSYWAR THINKING

Introduction

Chinese military analysts have meticulously studied the use of armed force during the 1991 Gulf War, the fight for Kosovo, and the recent fight in Iraq. [289] They have noted with great interest the integration of military strikes and psychological-warfare activities and the increased strategic role that the mass media played during both operations. [290]

To highlight the apparent shifting emphasis toward psychological warfare for PLA officers, the prominent Chinese military journal China Military Science has published more than six articles on psychological warfare since the year 2000: [291] "On PSYWAR in Recent High-Tech Local Wars," by Wang Zhenxing and Yang Suping; "The Doctrine of Psychological Operations in Ancient China," by Wu Juncang and Zhang Qiancheng; "Focus on Psychological War Against the Background of Grand Strategy," and "Psychological Operations in the Context of Grand Strategy," both written by Xu Hezhen; "Comparison of Psychological Warfare between China and the West," by Wang Lianshui, Ma Jingcheng, and Yan Jianhong; and "On Defense in Modern Psychological Warfare," by Li Yuankui, Wang Yanzheng, and Yang Xiaoli.

With the exception of Wu Juncang, Zhang Qiancheng, Wang Lianshui, Ma Jingcheng, and Yan Jianhong, the authors of the six articles are identified as being instructors at the Shijiazhuang Ground Forces Command Academy which indicates that the academy has an active and influential psychological-warfare department. In fact, judging by their tone, some of the articles could have been lifted directly from lectures presented during the academy's psychological-warfare courses. In addition, their use of some terms (for example, active defense) differs slightly from uses in previous chapters most likely because the majority of the PSYOP articles were from the 2000-2001 time frame.

The authors of the six articles suggest that at the strategic level, China's psychological-warfare operations will be characterized by coercion that will take the form of intimidation achieved through demonstrations and shows of force. (Their suggestion supports a recent Pentagon finding that viewed Chinese coercion as the greatest threat to Taiwan.)

---

[289] This chapter first appeared as an article titled "New Developments in Chinese Psychological Warfare" in Special Warfare, April 2003, pp. 9-17. It has been slightly modified.

[290] Wang Zhenxing and Yang Suping, "On PSYWAR in Recent High-Tech Local wars," Zhongguo Junshi Kexue (China Military Science), 20 December 2000, pp. 127-133, as translated and downloaded from the FBIS Web site on 8 March 2001.

[291] These articles form the basis for this discussion. The journal China Military Science is the rough equivalent of the US armed forces Joint Force Quarterly. One of the Chinese articles noted that the terms "psychological warfare" and "psychological operations" are interchangeable (which, of course, Western analysts would refute). This author uses the term "psychological warfare" because FBIS translators used the term more often than they used "psychological operations." One exception is the article by Wu Juncang and Zhang Qiancheng in which translators used the term "psychological operations" exclusively.

At the tactical level, the articles suggest that the Chinese are interested in offsetting their current deficiencies by procuring advanced psychological-warfare equipment and by developing advanced deployment techniques. The advanced equipment would include UAVs fitted with loudspeakers and capable of distributing "talking leaflets."

The articles also underscore the differences in the cultural and subjective-cognition patterns of Oriental and Western minds. Those differences lead the Chinese to apply the principles of psychological warfare differently from the West. If the US is to see "eye to eye" with the Chinese and truly understand their psychological-warfare methodology, it is vital that it comprehends those differences. Finally, the articles provide recommendations about the PLA's future psychological-warfare requirements. From the discussion in all six articles, it is clear that China is working hard to develop its psychological-warfare capabilities for peacetime and wartime uses.

History of Chinese PSYOP

In "The Doctrine of Psychological Operations in Ancient China," Wu Juncang and Zhang Qiancheng note that China's history of psychological operations goes back more than four thousand years. The authors point out that during the period 2100-256 B.C., psychological operations were part of such historical events as the Zhuolu War (Zhuolu is a county in Hebei Province), during which "victory could not be achieved with weapons"; the Tang Oath, under which Chinese swore to do everything possible to spread propaganda; and the Mu Oath, which prohibited the killing of enemy soldiers who surrendered or who were taken as prisoners of war—a psychological operation for that time period. Schemes for sowing deception and creating false impressions and expectations represented the acme of psychological operations during the period.[292]

According to Wu and Zhang, those early psychological experiences culminated in Sun Tzu's Art of War, which describes the main objective of war as defeating the enemy without having to fight; the main essence of war as attacking the enemy's strategy; the main principle of war as contending for control of hearts, minds and morale; and the main idea of war as focusing on the enemy commander's decision-making skills and personal traits. Ancient Chinese psychological-operations doctrine also focused on attacking the enemy's strategy and diplomacy, on conducting demonstrations and seeking dominance, on ignoring luck and dispelling doubt, on making threats, and on adhering to the Tao, the philosophy and system of religion based on the teachings of Lao-tzu during the sixth century B.C.[293]

Wu and Zhang indicate that Taoism, which coupled hardness with softness in warfare, was not the only influence on the theory of psychological operations in ancient China. Other influences were military studies, Confucianism (which stressed the idea of "just wars"), and the study of the I Ching (Book of Changes), which stressed the idea of

---

[292] Wu Juncang and Zhang Qiancheng, "The Doctrine of Psychological Operations in Ancient China," Zhongguo Junshi Kexue (China Military Science), Number 5 2002, pp. 88-94, as translated and downloaded from the FBIS Web site on 14 January 2002.
[293] Ibid.

yin and yang (hardness and softness) being coupled to each other and thereby changing each other. The I Ching formed an important theoretical foundation of psychological-operations doctrine in ancient China[294] that continues to influence subjective cognition patterns in China today.

According to Wu and Zhang, the Qin (221-206 B.C.) and Han (206 B.C.-8 A.D. and 25-220 A.D.) periods of Chinese history witnessed other types of psychological operations. The Qin period used the diplomatic psychological-operations strategy of maintaining friendly relations with distant enemies while attacking the enemy nearby. The Han dynasty integrated the political, economic, and military aspects of psychological operations, raising it to a new level.

The authors note the Three Kingdoms (220-280 A.D.) and the Two Jins (263-420 A.D.) for the diversity of their psychological-operations theory. Both dynasties believed that attacking the enemy's psychological state was more effective than attacking his cities; therefore, they favored psychological operations over combat operations with troops. The Ming (1368-1662) and Qing (1662-1912) dynasties, on the other hand, allowed Chinese psychological-operations doctrine to stagnate.[295]

Ancient Chinese books discuss the psychological-operations experiences of their time. For example, the Six Arts of War notes that in a command structure of seventy-two men, nineteen of them (26 percent) were psychological-operations personnel responsible for controlling morale. Of these, five were to tout the army's strength; four were to tout the army's fame in order to destroy the enemy's confidence; eight were to scout out the enemy's mood and intent; and two were to confuse the people by exploiting their belief in gods and spirits. The book also instructs Chinese soldiers to protect their morale by ignoring rumors, by disregarding luck, and by avoiding any dealings with omens or superstitions. The Six Arts also tells soldiers to sap enemy morale, to string enemy nerves, and to strike terror in the enemy. Wu and Zhang discuss two ancient tales that hint at the creativity of the Chinese in accomplishing these tasks. In the first tale, Chinese soldiers tied reed pipes to kites and flew the kites at night. The kites made a wailing sound that, in the darkness, unnerved the enemy. In the second tale, Chinese soldiers painted oxen in odd colors and tied oil-soaked reeds to the tails of the oxen. The soldiers lit the reeds and sent the enraged animals charging through the enemy camp at night, causing terror among the enemy soldiers.[296]

Wu and Zhang note that the Six Arts also refers to another key psychological aspect that should be attacked—the mind of the enemy's commanding general. While the Six Arts discusses the psychological condition of the commander at the strategic and tactical levels differently, it lists intelligence, temperament, and moral character as the three main characteristics required of a Chinese commander.[297] The book also lists ten

---

[294] Ibid.
[295] Ibid.
[296] Ibid.
[297] Ibid.

psychological weaknesses of commanders that must be exploited. Those weaknesses include being brave, treating death too lightly, being impatient, and thinking too quickly.

According to Wu and Zhang, the Marxist concept of the "dialectic"—the process of change brought about by the conflict of opposing forces—had a significant impact on the development of ancient Chinese psychological-operations theory, although that fact was not "discovered" until the advent of Marxism. The authors note that ancient doctrine involved many categories of contradictions out of which evolved many of the principles and methods of psychological operations.[298] Although ancient, Sun Zi's Art of War, Wu Zi's Art of War, and Weiliao Zi and Sun Bin's Art of War provide incisive and comprehensive explanations of the objectives, principles, methods and laws of psychological operations, and their explanations are still valid.

In summarizing their understanding of ancient Chinese psychological operations, Wu and Zhang maintain that those operations were designed to achieve strategic deception, to map out a strategy, to secure victory through strategy, and to integrate military strategy and psychological attack.[299] The authors find these objectives or activities of ancient Chinese psychological-operations doctrine to be reflective of what the Chinese observed during the Gulf War and during the fight for Kosovo, further emphasizing the importance of psychological operations in the modern era.

Definitions

Each of the Chinese articles on psychological operations defines the concepts of psychological warfare or psychological operations in a different way. Wu Juncang and Zhang Qiancheng (who do not teach at the Shijiazhuang Academy) define a psychological operation as the use of various measures to influence a combat opponent's ideology, attitude, will, or actions. The objective of a psychological operation is to win without fighting or to win a big victory with only a little fighting. Only by securing a favorable position in terms of politics and in terms of the nature of warfare (by making one's own side's reasons for war to appear to be moral and just) can one achieve a fundamental psychological advantage.[300]

Xu Hezhen, a major general in the Chinese army and president of the Shijiazhuang Academy, defines psychological warfare as a kind of propaganda, and as persuasion that uses real force as its foundation. According to Xu's definition, a group can use political, economic, scientific, military, diplomatic, ideological, or cultural forces to change an opponent's national will or to influence and change an opponent's belief in, attitude toward, or hostility toward a populace, toward organizations, or toward military and government agencies. Xu's two articles stress the need for using power and

---

[298] Ibid.
[299] Ibid.
[300] Ibid.

intimidation as key psychological-warfare tools.[301] Regarding the importance of psychological warfare, Xu notes: "You may not be interested in psychological warfare, but psychological warfare is interested in you."[302]

According to Xu, psychological warfare is also the exploration and study of the psychological quality of the thinking practiced by a nation's strategic leadership. To the Chinese, psychological quality includes the aspects of psychological attainments and psychological character. Psychological attainments primarily reflect the level at which a person grasps and understands psychology. Psychological character is the individual human aspect, primarily the psychological character that an individual has already formed or is developing; e.g., an individual's intellect, temperament, disposition, emotions, and will.[303]

Xu notes that Eastern psychological attainments are developed through education in both dialectical materialism and historical materialism, and through the influence and edifying effects of Eastern culture. His theory applies particularly to strategic thought, in which "how to think" is the key element and the most valuable quality.[304] Xu agrees that, in the end, the most important battles of modern psychological war will be fought over values. The superpowers, he feels, are using armed force to impose their value systems on other people. This was demonstrated during operations in Kosovo, in Xu's opinion, when politicians used the idea that human rights are greater than sovereign rights.[305]

After 50 years of Marxism, Xu notes:

Decadent culture has unavoidably entered China. … Foreign culture has constantly infiltrated China in the form of weapons and then at the mental and conceptual level. In particular, the value system of Western culture, with the idea of individualism at the center, a decadent lifestyle based on materialism, and a concept of gain or benefit in interpersonal relations, has produced a profound effect on certain people's values.[306]

Wang Lianshui, Ma Jingcheng, and Yan Jianhong, the other three authors who are not identified as being faculty of the Shijiazhuang Academy, define psychological-warfare theory as a field of study that serves both as the point of intersection and as the boundary line between psychology and the study of strategy and tactics. In their opinion, psychological-warfare theory has a psychological foundation as well as an ideological/theoretical foundation. The latter foundation is determined by national characteristics, but the former foundation is more constant. Psychological-warfare

---

[301] Xu Hezhen, "Focus on Psychological War Against the Background of Grand Strategy," Zhongguo Junshi Kexue (China Military Science), Number 5 2000, pp. 67-76, as translated and downloaded from the FBIS Web site on 11 December 2000.
[302] Xu Hezhen, "Psychological Operations in the Context of Grand Strategy," Zhongguo Junshi Kexue (China Military Science), 30 September 2001, pp. 94-100, as translated and downloaded from the FBIS Web site on 21 November 2001.
[303] Xu Hezhen, "Psychological Operations in the Context of Grand Strategy."
[304] Ibid.
[305] Xu Hezhen, "Focus on Psychological War…"
[306] Ibid.

strategy is a psychological embodiment of the orientation of a country's national and military strategies. [307]

Li Yuankui, a Senior Colonel at the Shijiazhuang Academy, and two master's-degree candidates, Lieutenant Wang Yanzheng and Lieutenant Yang Xiaoli, define psychological warfare as a multilevel activity that is employed at the strategic, operational, and tactical levels. The authors perceive the targets of psychological warfare as national will, the state of social awareness, cultural traditions, a nation's economic pulse, an opponent's public sentiment, the tendencies of popular will, military morale, and the opponent's various social groups, classes and strata. Because of the increased use of information technology, the number of people who are subjected to psychological war is greater than ever before.[308] The increase in psychological-warfare targets requires the development of a people's war-defense mentality.

Li, Wang, and Yang, like Xu, focus on values. They define a system of values as a system of psychological tendencies that people use to discriminate between good and bad. A system of values also provides the basis by which a person recognizes the correct way of thinking and acting. The highest strategic objective in psychological warfare, the authors note, is achieved by changing a country's fundamental social concepts and its society's sense of values. In this regard, the West uses a system of values (democracy, freedom, human rights, etc.) in a long-term attack on socialist countries. The West used the ideas of democracy and human rights to undermine the communist party in the Soviet Union, and it intends to use the same rationale for interfering in China's internal affairs. The US's strategy is to attack political, moral, social, and cultural values in target countries.[309] Chinese authors are fond of quoting former US President Richard Nixon's phrase, "Attacking ideas is key to affecting history" as an explanation of US strategy.

Senior Colonel Wang Zhenxing and Major Yang Suping of the Shijiazhuang Academy did not define psychological warfare or psychological operations in their article.

Psychological Security

A key aspect of conducting psychological warfare is to understand the psychological characteristics of an opponent's strategic leadership and to conduct psychological attacks against them.[310] Authors Wang Lianshui, Ma Jingcheng, and Yan Jianhong discuss differences in Eastern and Western minds in order to highlight East/West variances both in the characteristics and in the laws of psychological warfare.

---

[307] Wang Lianshui, Ma Jingcheng and Yan Jianhong, "Comparison of Psychological Warfare between China and the West," Zhongguo Junshi Kexue (China Military Science), Number 6 2000, pp. 102-110, as translated and downloaded from the FBIS Web site on 25 June 2001.
[308] Li Yuankui, Wang Yanzheng and Yang Xiaoli, "On Defense in Modern Psychological Warfare," Zhongguo Junshi Kexue (China Military Science), Number 6 2000, pp. 117-126, as translated and downloaded from the FBIS Web site on 8 March 2001.
[309] Ibid.
[310] Xu Hezhen, "Psychological Operations in the Context of Grand Strategy."

The authors note, "Differences in environment, cultural traditions, political systems, economic strength, national-defense capability and national spiritual belief lead to a great distinction in various nations in subjective cognition, ideological basis, principles of applications and structure of organization of psychological warfare."[311]

According to the authors, even though China is a socialist country, the Marxist theory of war provides the theoretical basis for Chinese psychological warfare and gives Chinese psychological warfare its advanced, moral, open, and unified nature.[312] Marxist theory regarding proletarian strategy and tactics was one of Mao Zedong's "magic weapons" during the Chinese revolution. And even though psychological warfare in the opinion of Wang, Ma, and Yan is characterized by active defense, China's approach emphasizes psychological attacks and the use of stratagems, particularly the use of deception activities.[313]

Marxist theory opposes peaceful evolution, which the authors assert is the basic Western tactic for subverting socialist countries. According to Wang, Ma, and Yan, peaceful evolution is the process that caused the disintegration of the Soviet Union, and the Chinese must not allow peaceful evolution to take place in China. The authors note that Mao Zedong and Deng Xiaoping developed a theory and a complete set of tactics designed to counter the Western strategy.

In "On Defense in Modern Psychological Warfare," Li, Wang, and Yang emphasize that China must take the initiative in psychological-warfare defense because psychological security is now an important aspect of national security. Information and psychological factors are now political and diplomatic weapons, and their power cannot be ignored. Psychological warfare requires a low investment; it involves low risk; and it is highly effective. The greater the amount of information that is available to a population, the more room there will be for psychological warfare. Any corner into which information can spread can become a battlefield for psychological warfare. China must establish the strategic idea of an active psychological-warfare defense.

Active defense according to Li, Wang, and Yang should include tempering the minds of the Chinese people by inoculation: allowing the people to come into contact with other ideas and, through education and guidance, allowing them to see what is wrong with those ideas. That approach will allow people to develop psychological immunity. Opening their minds up to other ideas, however, is not the same as cutting them loose.[314]

Li, Wang, and Yang forecast that the main form of psychological warfare will be contests for public opinion. To be able to seize public opinion, China must develop its own independent information and media power, guide public opinion, and conduct public-opinion propaganda. The demand for information is a universal psychological

---

[311] Wang Lianshui, Ma Jingcheng and Yan Jianhong.
[312] Ibid.
[313] Ibid.
[314] Li Yuankui, Wang Yanzheng, and Yang Xiaoli.

need. Passive psychological defense will not suffice. Only with initiative and offense can China take the strategic initiative with regard to public opinion. Propaganda must be prepared in advance, and it must include material designed to counter the attacks that will be made against the initial release of propaganda.[315]

In "On PSYWAR in Recent High-Tech Local Wars," Wang and Yang emphasize the importance of attaining media superiority and of controlling the negative effects of media coverage. Media control will be one of the front lines in psychological wars. News broadcasts and computer technology now allow people to watch a battle in progress, as they would watch a sporting event. Millions can now witness an event that might have been known to only a few people in the past. Such access to information affects public sentiment and morale. Wang and Yang accuse the West of fulfilling its hegemonic wishes by manipulating public opinion, by attaining media superiority, and by guiding people's psychological tendencies.[316] Yet all three methods are exactly what the Chinese are proud to claim elsewhere as their heritage.

According to Xu Hezhen in "Focus on Psychological War Against the Background of Grand Strategy," intimidation is a key strategy that can be used to influence both public opinion and the media. In fact, psychological war and intimidation are so difficult to tell apart that they are almost twins. Intimidation is both a strategy and a method according to Xu. In modern times, the use of nonviolent intimidation, which includes alliances, media manipulation, economic sanctions, financial attack, information isolation, and network attacks, has increased.

The US, Xu says, uses its advantage of power as the foundation of psychological war, employing arms displays, arms sales, and military exercises as intimidation.[317] In response, China must implement its own psychological intimidation war plan that includes Chinese threat forces and mechanisms, and psychological intimidation war strategy.[318] China should develop an elite and effective military intimidation force, fully apply all kinds of nonmilitary intimidation methods, establish a psychological intimidation mechanism that will have strategic maneuvering as its core, and organize and apply all kinds of psychological intimidation factors, thus developing the greatest psychological intimidation effect. Intimidation must be established on the foundation of power; without power, intimidation is only a scarecrow.[319]

Strategy

In "The Doctrine of Psychological Operations in Ancient China," Wu Juncang and Zhang Qiancheng argue that strategy is fundamental and that mapping out a strategy is the most traditional Chinese characteristic of psychological warfare. Mapping out the strategy is followed by attacking an opponent's alliances, attacking his army, and attacking his cities—in that order. The best strategy is to attack the enemy's mind,

---

[315] Ibid.
[316] Wang Zhenxing and Yang Suping.
[317] Xu Hezhen, "Focus on Psychological War…"
[318] Ibid.
[319] Ibid.

leaving him unable to plan. Strategy can create psychological misperceptions that will cause one side to remain unprepared. The prepared side can then win without fighting. In a more narrow sense, the use of strategy may be seen in demonstrations and feints that surprise the enemy by hitting him where he is unprepared.[320]

Authors Wang, Ma, and Yan see major differences between China and the West regarding the strategic starting points and the orientation of psychological warfare. By strategic[321] starting points, the authors mean psychological warfare's nature, objectives, and factors for victory. China, the authors say, looks at psychological warfare as a method of spreading truth and justice; of trying to win people's minds; and of exposing an enemy's plot to confuse, corrupt or penetrate China's mental space. The West, the authors contend, views psychological warfare as a way of promoting its hegemonic strategy that is designed to create turmoil and division within other countries. (Clearly, more than a few Western analysts would disagree with that categorization.)

Wang, Ma, and Yan list two strategic orientations: offensive and defensive. The orientations differ in their roles, in their employment, and in the structure of their deployment. China must continue to combine offense with defense, and to use offense for defense (so that the country can shift from passive to active modes and expand its room for maneuver).

From Wu and Zhang's perspective, demonstrations and shows of force are the basic strategic methods of conducting psychological operations. Demonstrations were used in ancient times, as detailed in discussions of the thirty-six stratagems of war in ancient times. A demonstration is an attack that exploits strengths and weaknesses, and its objective is to take the enemy by surprise. One may exploit strengths and weaknesses by appearing to be strong when one is weak, or by appearing to be weak when one is strong.[322] In short, demonstrations are a way of getting friendly and enemy forces to interact psychologically. Demonstrations are also a form of deterrence, which is another psychological-warfare concept. Demonstrations establish credibility and fear, two of the three elements of deterrence theory (reliability is the third).

Strategy's essence, according to Xu, is thinking, and the quality of one's thinking determines the quality of one's strategy. Strategic thinking is a big-picture, integrated method of thought, a bird's-eye-view way of thinking. It is anticipatory, realistic and response oriented, and it is a kind of rational thinking.[323]

Information Technology

Information technology has made it possible for psychological warfare to become both a strategic resource and a method, and psychological specialists are exploiting many information-age technologies. For example, future military attacks will be combined with

---

[320] Wu Juncang and Zhang Qiancheng.
[321] Wang Lianshui, Ma Jingcheng, and Yan Jianhong.
[322] Wu Juncang and Zhang Qiancheng.
[323] Xu Hezhen, "Psychological Operations in the Context of Grand Strategy."

attacks on electronic technology; virtual reality will plant false information in an enemy's command-information system, creating misperceptions among commanders; and network intruders may be able to penetrate terminals on the network, executing an all-directional psychological attack.[324]

According to Wang and Yang, "In modern times the vast development in information science, psychology, the science of broadcasting, and other sciences, and in particular the emergence of new and high technologies such as satellite communications, electronic computers, networking technology, and multimedia technology, provide a firm theoretical foundation and modern tools for psychological warfare."[325]

Li, Wang, and Yang see networks as the most important aspect of the technological battle. Network psychological warfare is a new topic in psychological-warfare defense, but networks will become the main psychological-warfare battlefield in the future. Global networks provide more space in which to engage in propaganda. Network data can be put online in secrecy by almost anyone; it is difficult to verify who the providers of network data are; and access to information is not subject to restrictions of time or place. Network attacks can throw a country's social, political, and economic life into chaos, producing a shock effect on people's minds and leading to political instability. In order to develop network defense, China must develop network sovereignty, establish laws for network activities, and establish information-protection forces. Creating competent forces for information war and psychological warfare will help ensure China's information security and psychological security.[326]

Writing about the impact of information technology, Wang and Yang list several futuristic ideas for psychological-warfare equipment, but they do not specify whether the ideas are theirs or those of another country. They note that an "intelligent" component has been added to psychological-warfare equipment. The intelligent component includes computers used to guide the operating and sensing systems of UAVs. UAVs can recognize targets, broadcast propaganda, and scatter leaflets before returning to their base. In the future, leaflets will combine visual, audio, and speech elements (perhaps the reference here is to products like the talking birthday cards marketed by US card manufacturers). In a direct reference to US technology, the authors note that Livermore Laboratories has developed a method of projecting holographic images high into the clouds. According to Wang and Yang, the projections produce a type of illusory psychological warfare by portraying Islamic martyrs who appear to speak to soldiers from the clouds.[327]

In contemporary wars, such as the Gulf War, the first targets attacked have been targets with psychological value, such as television, broadcasting, and other communications venues. Destruction of those targets helped cause psychological passivity, panic and, eventually, defeat. Russia underestimated the power of

---

[324] Wang Zhenxing and Yang Suping.
[325] Ibid.
[326] Li Yuankui, Wang Yanzheng and Yang Xiaoli.
[327] Wang Zhenxing and Yang Suping.

communications during its first war with Chechnya from 1994-96. The Chechens were able to exert a major psychological influence on the course and the outcome of the war by utilizing the impact of instantaneous field reporting to TV stations. That reporting greatly affected public opinion.[328] TV also played a major role in the Gulf War, demonstrating the lethality of coalition weaponry to the Iraqi leadership. On the other hand, TV reports on Iraqi Scuds also played a significant psychological role by invoking terror and panic among the residents of Israel and Saudi Arabia.[329]

Threats

General Xu Hezhen's article, "Psychological Operations in the Context of Grand Strategy," describes the threats facing China, which he labeled as "hard warfare" (high-tech warfare) and "soft warfare" (psychological warfare designed to "westernize" or "split" China). Xu notes that while the former is the most difficult, the latter could be accomplished in the context of a grand strategy in which psychological warfare plays an increasingly important role in safeguarding national security and in winning high-tech wars.[330]

Because psychological war can achieve the greatest number of political benefits and the greatest psychological influence while taking almost no risks, Xu believes that the US is using a psychological-warfare strategy—peaceful evolution—to enhance the disintegration of socialist countries. He says that as part of that strategy, the US has developed a military force that possesses advanced weapons, and that the US has carried out violent psychological threats toward socialist nations. According to Xu, the US has used economics and trade to infiltrate socialist nations and has used personnel exchanges to carry out ideological and cultural psychological infiltration, thereby fostering an anti-socialist force.

According to Xu, US psychological warfare undermined the Soviet Union, and he sees evidence of a similar threat to China during the last two US presidential administrations. While the Clinton era focused on engaging China, Xu says, the Bush administration has a clear strategic goal of containing China.[331] Finally, in Xu's opinion, the US is using religion to weaken the ideology of Marxism.[332]

Of course, the greatest psychological-warfare threat is the threat of taking control of morale, the foundation stone for victory, according to Wu and Zhang. They describe five tactics for controlling morale:

- With a mighty opponent, wait him out.
- With an arrogant opponent, show him respect for a long time.
- With a firm opponent, entice and then seize him.

---

[328] Ibid.
[329] Ibid.
[330] Xu Hezhen, "Psychological Operations in the Context of Grand Strategy."
[331] Ibid.
[332] Ibid.

- With an evasive opponent, get close to him in front, make noise on his flanks, dig deep ditches and put up high ramparts, and make it hard for him to get provisions.
- With a placid opponent, make noise to frighten him, jolt him by breaking through, and if he comes at you, then attack him, otherwise, fall back.[333]

Chinese Recommendations on PSYOP

The foregoing discussion indicates that the theory of psychological warfare has tremendous significance and value to China. Chinese theorists are attempting to develop an updated ideology and strategy of psychological warfare—one that will focus on intimidation and on exploitation of the differences between Eastern and Western mentalities. That implies that China will be establishing a command structure for psychological warfare, as well as creating special units that will attempt to overcome Chinese inferiority in high-tech weapons.[334] More important, Chinese theorists appear to believe that because modern psychological warfare can help ensure stability and shape national-security thinking, it is more applicable in peace than in war.[335]

In offering recommendations for future psychological-warfare forces in China, Major General Xu asks Chinese leaders to:

- Develop a psychological warfare system that integrates specialization and non-specialization personnel, and that possesses the special characteristics of China
- Establish at the national level a guiding coordination agency for psychological war, and carry out unified guidance and coordination of the national psychological war actions
- Establish a psychological war command agency under the unified leadership of the Central Military Commission and party committee
- Establish psychological war scientific research agencies of all natures to guide the work nationally and in the military
- Establish a specialized psychological corps, forming a consolidated and effective psychological attack force
- Develop a modernized psychological-war material and technical equipment basis and
- Launch a new emphasis on psychological war education for the masses and all commanders in the military, forming a people's psychological war. [336]

According to Wang and Yang, China has many psychological-warfare shortcomings to overcome. Those include the backwardness and the nonspecialization of its current psychological-operations forces, a lack of talent, and the lack of a unified and coordinated psychological-warfare command. Wang and Yang also believe that China lacks a unified understanding of the strategic role of psychological warfare and of the role that psychological warfare can play in high-tech local wars.[337]

---

[333] Wu Juncang and Zhang Qiancheng.
[334] Ibid.
[335] Xu Hezhen, "Focus on Psychological War."
[336] Ibid.
[337] Wang Zhenxing and Yang Suping.

Wang, Ma, and Yan believe that in order for China to overcome its weakness in equipment, materials, and technical content, it must develop a force that combines its mass-action strength with a specialized structure for psychological warfare.[338] Overall, China's shortcomings are hindering the development of a coordinated psychological-warfare strategy for the PLA.

Apparently, other nations have noticed China's focus on psychological warfare and have responded. In January 2002, Taiwan, taking advice from US military officials, activated its first modern psychological-warfare unit to counter China's buildup.[339] The existing Taiwanese psychological-operations unit is part of the political-warfare department.

Finally, China will continue to view the US as its major psychological-warfare threat. Xu says that the US's objective is to gain benefits from the Chinese consumer market and to maintain long-term political and psychological pressure on China. The US will accomplish that objective by attacking China's national self-respect and by compelling China to do what the US asks.[340] Xu warns the Chinese that psychological acceptance of socialism depends on China's comprehensive national strength and on the level of progress that the social system achieves in economic development and in socialist awakening. He says that one cannot believe that "the foreign moon is rounder than our own," for this is defeatist psychology. Conviction in the correctness of one's own system is what works and that is what is required.[341]

In the end, we should not expect China to waver from the main characteristics of its psychological-warfare doctrine: strong reliance on the use of war experience; deep cultural roots; influence of Marxist materialist dialectics; and a reliance on strategic deception.[342] These characteristics also include a reliance on ancient experience in applying strategies as a primary psychological warfare methodology and a reliance on the use of intimidation backed by power.

China will use power projection as a means of achieving success in influencing the activities of foreign nations. Its centralized leadership system will continue to exert control over the news, propaganda, and public opinion.[343] Most important for Western analysts to comprehend is that Chinese theorists "think" strategically in a way that few foreigners do. Western analysts will have to come to terms with this fact if they hope to learn to first understand and then predict Chinese psychological-warfare strategy in the coming years.

---

[338] Wang Lianshui, Ma Jingcheng, and Yan Jianhong.
[339] Brian Hsu, Taipei Times (Internet Version), 7 December 2001, as translated and downloaded from the FBIS Web site on 7 December 2001.
[340] Xu Hezhen, "Focus on Psychological War."
[341] Ibid.
[342] Wu Juncang and Zhang Qiancheng.
[343] Wang Lianshui, Ma Jingcheng, and Yan Jianhong.

This discussion of China's view of psychological operations completes the overview of IW through 2003. It is now time to consider what Chinese military analysts had to say about the coalition's use of IW during the March-April 2003 fighting in Iraq. Chinese comments are broken into two parts. Chapter Six covers the March and April 2003 period, when there was probably more pure reporting than analysis. Chapter Seven covers the May through August period and is representative of a more measured and analytical view of "lessons learned." Chinese analysts who observed and reported on the war discuss all of the major topics covered in the chapters to date—IW, strategies, PSYOP, and so on.

CHAPTER SIX: THE COALITION BATTLE FOR IRAQ (MARCH–APRIL 2003)

Introduction

During NATO's conflict with Serbia over Kosovo in 1999 described in Chapter One, and during the more recent conflict between the US-led coalition and Iraq, Chinese analysts took great care to measure the tactics and strategies used by both sides. These analysts also suggested what China should learn from these encounters. Interestingly, some of China's best-known IW analysts did a significant portion of the reporting.

Chinese Perceptions of the War in Iraq

The war in Iraq unleashed a barrage of commentary and lessons learned from varying perspectives. This chapter will focus on Chinese perspectives of the coalition battle for Iraq in the March-April 2003 period. It will be more comprehensive than the strictly IW analysis devoted to Kosovo in Chapter One because there is more information to analyze. Predictably, the Chinese focus is on "how to fight" —the strategy and tactics used. As the Chinese have pointed out on several occasions, while the Western tendency is to focus on technology, the Chinese focus, both culturally and historically, is on stratagems.

Both the strengths and weaknesses of coalition and Iraqi forces are examined. Further, there is a focus on media coverage of the war that is also predictable. Recent Chinese information-warfare writings have placed great emphasis on psychological operations and the media, and this war was an example for Chinese military theorists to consider. Finally, a host of "lessons learned" conferences were held in China on the conduct and outcome of the fighting.

A variety of Chinese sources were responsible for these articles describing coalition and Iraqi actions. Some were simply the views of reporters while others were more authoritative voices from the National Defense University or from the People's Liberation Army. One person in particular, military expert Fan Gaoyue, produced the most memorable analysis. He correctly predicted many coalition actions to include the prediction on 1 April 2003 that the battle for Baghdad would be "a swift and decisive battle." Others were not quite as adept as Fan and made serious mistakes in their predictions. Overall, however, it is clear that the Chinese are eager to learn from the Iraqi conflict and to adapt their fighting machine as necessary.

Strategy and Tactics

Even before the war started, Chinese newspapers offered advice to Iraq on how to fight coalition forces. One unlikely source, Zhongguo Qingnian Bao, sponsored by the China Youth League of the Chinese Communist Party Central Committee, discussed six tricks that Iraq could use. These so-called tricks were really nothing more than tactical advice, but they could be considered as stratagems. Two of the tricks involved luring coalition forces into cities where noncontact war would not work. In particular Somalia was cited as an example of how to fight against Americans. Other tactical advice included cutting apart and surrounding coalition forces on the move, using deceptive measures, looking for mistakes in logistical arrangements and weaknesses in the complicated command structure of the coalition, and using the environment and topography as a protective screen.[344]

The Hong Kong T'ai Yang Pao wrote in February 2003 that Iraqi forces could not meet coalition forces head on and should fight a defensive, guerilla, or street war in order to have a chance at success. Frontal wars and fierce battles should be avoided. The Iraqi armed forces should keep its strength and expect to fight a sustained war. A key strategy of Iraqi President Saddam Hussein would be to generate enough casualties (one hundred would cause large scale demonstrations, while one thousand might cause US President George Bush to resign). Thus the fighting "will" of the Iraqis would be a decisive factor. If Hussein could mobilize the entire army and his people, the article noted, then the Chinese military could again demonstrate that Mao Zedong's "thinking on People's War" is not outdated.[345] At the end of the war, Chinese journalists returned to this theme of People's War.

Other analysts provided advice to the coalition. One such analyst, Kou Liyan, looked at four problems facing the coalition: to capture Hussein alive or kill him; to try to save Iraq's oil fields; to avoid Hussein's possible use of biochemical weapons; and to reduce potential street fights.[346] Liu Dingping, a military officer who had observed the four conflicts in which the US participated since the end of the Cold War, noted that America had helped move China out of "just war" thinking and into "modern electronic warfare." Learning from these conflicts, China felt that the more the US fights, the smaller is the disparity between Chinese and American forces. To attack the coalition would require developing armaments by leaps and bounds, and striking the enemy at its "death points" or automated equipment. Liu underscored the necessity to invest in information warfare and to ensure means to disrupt an opponent's combat plans by way of electronic countermeasures and network attacks. This officer believed that there would not be much difference between how this war would be conducted and the one that broke out in 1991.[347]

Not surprisingly, the coalition's change in tactics to an immediate ground assault was the subject of one of the first articles after the opening salvos of the war. One reporter questioned why the US had changed its tactics, asking if it had an ace in the hole or if there was something the US was hiding. The author reached the conclusion that the

---

[344] Wei Yuejiang and Li Haiying, "Can the Six Tricky Moves Break with the Fairy Tale of Zero Casualty?", Zhongguo Qingnian Bao (Internet version), 18 January 2003, as translated and downloaded from the FBIS Web site on 21 January 2003.
[345] Ku Lu, "The Military Hopes Iraq will Fight a Guerrilla War and Reemphasize the 'People's War'", Hong Kong T'ai Yang Pao (Internet version), 19 February 2003, as translated and downloaded from the FBIS Web site on 19 February 2003.
[346] Kou Liyan, "New Tactics will be Used in a 'Topple Saddam' War," Renmin Ribao (People's Daily), 27 February 2003, p. 13, as translated and downloaded from the FBIS Web site on 27 February 2003.
[347] Liu Dingping, "What Should the Chinese Military Learn from US Wars?" Nanfang Zhoumo, 13 March 2003, p. A10, as translated and downloaded from the FBIS Web site on 20 March 2003.

US military remains flexible and employs electronic warfare "in obedience to and in the service of the main combat action." By not cutting off all Iraqi communications, the coalition force could still obtain intelligence from radio communications within Iraq and better understand the activities of Iraqi government officials. Thus, the reporter noted that the particular characteristics of targets in this conflict have altered the coalition's traditional way of doing business.[348]

Further, the Xinhua Domestic News Service reported that Iraq had learned several lessons from the 1991 war and had made significant flexible preparations for specific battles in Iraq. First, on 15 March, under orders from Hussein, the country was broken into four districts. This allowed military units to have more autonomy in case communications were lost, prevented the disarray of troop formations, and prevented soldiers from collapsing and surrendering. The Iraqi strategy was listed as "fortifying defenses, harnessing strengths, avoiding weaknesses, slowing the advance of US troops by every possible means, and defeating the enemy in urban warfare." Second, Hussein reorganized his division-based armed forces into brigades. Third, he decided to defend Baghdad and other large and medium cities. Multiple defensive belts were established around cities and in important areas within the cities. Air defense forces were beefed up. They utilized the tactics of "masking the true situation, presenting a false front, burrowing into mountains, and hiding underground." Finally, the Iraqi military planned to go underground and build up its strength while coalition aircraft conducted air strikes. It was less certain if Iraq would blow dams, use biochemical weapons, launch strikes against Israel, or set oil fields ablaze.[349] Military deception, it appeared from the Chinese analysis, would form the major aspect of the IW effort against the coalition.

Chinese writers were very interested in the use of guerrilla tactics by Iraq's forces due to their reliance on People's War tactics. They underscored the psychological and political toll that such a strategy would offer, and the fact that such a conflict could grow more complex even as the coalition moved toward victory. Perhaps guerrilla war is all that Hussein has left, the Chinese pondered, since sanctions had produced a weakly armed and motivated armed force with little fighting capabilities.[350] In spite of this fact, Chinese National Defense University scholars Wang Wen and Li Dajun underscored that Iraqi troops fought more determinedly than expected, but that it was unlikely the troops could effectively obstruct the coalition advance. They underscored Iraqi successes, noting that:

- With regard to war preparations, Iraq had fostered in troops the idea of fighting to the end.
- With regard to operational preparations, the Iraqi armed forces divided into smaller units.

---

[348] Tian Zhaoyun, "Notes on the War in Iraq: Why no Large-Scale Electronic Warfare This Time?" <u>Xinhua Domestic Service</u>, 0817 GMT 21 March 2003, as translated and downloaded from the FBIS Web site on 21 March 2003.

[349] Gu Dewei, "How Will Iraq Respond to the United States Militarily?" <u>Xinhua Domestic Service,</u> 1046 GMT 21 March 2003, as translated and downloaded from the FBIS Web site on 21 March 2003.

[350] "Saddam's Guerrillas Will Test US Resolve," <u>South China Morning Post</u> (Internet version), 25 March 2003, as translated and downloaded from the FBIS Web site on 25 March 2003.

- With regard to the method of fighting, Iraqi forces launched surprise attacks.
- With regard to air defense, Iraq had surveillance and tracking radars play a role in issuing early warnings of surprise attacks.
- And with regard to defensive operations, Iraqi forces integrated fire systems with defensive works and succeeded in counterattacks as well.[351]

Both Wang and Li predicted a quick move to Baghdad, and then a long and costly battle by coalition forces in order to take the city.[352]

By 26 March, Chinese writers were noting that the US must have forgotten some of the lessons learned from Vietnam (quick decisive victory) and that the Iraqis had learned that People's War theory was still applicable in the year 2003. The tactics used by Iraq, according to one writer, were:

- To induce the enemy to go deep and strike at its soft spot. (The Iraqi army reportedly left their places of work and hid underground or moved to the center of the country and awaited orders.)
- To break up the whole into parts, decentralizing the command. (Some Iraqi divisions disappeared without a trace, and the Chinese believed the units had broken up into smaller parts.)
- To introduce the model of street battles. (There were snipers, army personnel in civilian clothes, etc.)
- To produce results using guerrilla warfare. (This included targeting US troops that drop behind, feigning surrender, and starting assaults when coalition troops were not prepared.)
- To dampen US forces' morale. (This was done by showing captured US prisoners of war on TV and broadcasting photos via Al-Jazirah to the Arab world.)[353]

This Chinese commentary of a comparison with the fighting in Vietnam came after 23 March, a day the Chinese viewed as the toughest day of the fighting. Fighting against the coalition at that time were not just the Iraqi armed forces, they noted, but also Saddam's suicidal commandos and Baath Party militias.[354] It was intense fighting that forced the coalition to adjust its plans, according to the Chinese, not the weather or lack of logistics. They felt the coalition must worry about supply lines and threats to key southern cities. For the coalition, this signaled that the gloves were off and that cities to be "liberated" were now listed as "military objectives." Hussein's forces were accused of not fighting fair. The Chinese offered to broker an arrangement with Baghdad, noting that

[351] Luan Hai, "Our Country's Experts Comment on Gains, Losses of US, Iraqi Troops in their Attack-Defense Operations," Xinhua Domestic Service, 1123 GMT 25 March 2003, as translated and downloaded from the FBIS Web site on 25 March 2003.
[352] Ibid.
[353] Qiu Yongzheng, "Saddam's Five Tactics for Resisting US Forces," Qingnian Cankao (Internet version), 26 March 2003, as translated and downloaded from the FBIS Web site on 27 March 2003.
[354] Ren Yujun, "Coalition Forces begin to Taste the Bitter Fruit of Guerrilla Warfare," Renmin Ribao, 26 March 2003, p. 3, as translated and downloaded from the FBIS Web site on 26 March 2003.

it might not be the victory the coalition sought, but it was preferable to continuation of fighting an unwinnable war.[355]

The Chinese analysis demonstrated that as soon as coalition forces suffered problems, Chinese theoreticians wanted to tell them why. Foremost among the list of reasons for coalition failures was the inability to understand guerrilla war, Chinese analysts noted. National Defense University Strategic Studies Research Institute expert Lin Bo wrote an article typical of such responses on 27 March. First, he noted that last minute changes in the coalition's prebattle deployment were a big mistake and one of a strategist's great taboos. Lin noted that within the next few days US forces would start moving much slower. Second, Lin stated that the coalition overestimated its real strength, and this was a problem. Further, ground troops were thrown in too soon. Lin believed that things would get difficult for the coalition once the war reached the stage of urban operations or guerrilla fighting. Third, outdated equipment would cause the combat casualty rate to climb. (As hard as it might be to believe, Lin charged the US military with obsolete equipment!) Finally information-system problems arose. Lin said they included friendly fire attacks and the recurrence of misdirected attacks due to problems with identification systems and interference with the global positioning system.[356]

In another review of US military setbacks, it was noted that the coalition forces made four mistakes. They attacked too hastily; they underestimated the Iraqi forces; they attempted to use "trickery" (decapitation and a frightening missile attack); and they sent in ground forces too early.[357] In addition, the Chinese writer noted that now the coalition would have to meet the Republican Guard in Baghdad and engage them in street fighting. He also felt that "experts" who predicted that the war would end in a few weeks were way off base. Again, these "mistakes" by the Chinese writer show how hard it is to predict anything in wartime when events are unfolding. It is better to wait until events are completed before going into detailed analysis of what has or will occur. Initial impressions are often wrong, as were the predictions of most Chinese military analysts.

Finally, on 16 April, Professor Zhang Zhaozhong added that since Hussein did not have a scorched-earth policy (destroying bridges, water reservoirs, etc.), then Iraq had either concealed its army among the people and was waiting to attack, or there was a complete strategic dispersal by the Iraqi forces and a counterattack was being planned. Additionally, according to Zhang, the media was controlling what the viewer could see.[358]

---

[355] "In Iraq, the Gloves are Now Coming Off," South China Morning Post (Internet version), 27 March 2003, as translated and downloaded from the FBIS Web site on 27 March 2003.

[356] Lin Bo, "Why the US Military has Made Repeated Miscalculations," Renmin Ribao, 27 March 2003, p. 3, as translated and downloaded from the FBIS Web site on 27 March 2003.

[357] Kung Yao-wen, "How Can One Not Meet with Trouble if One is Arrogant and Conceited?" Ta Kung Pao (Internet version), 30 March 2003, as translated and downloaded from the FBIS Web site on 31 March 2003.

[358] Jian Zheng, Liang Ping, and Qiu Yongzheng, "Zhang Zhaozhong: War is Studied in Order to Stop War," Qingnian Cankao (Internet Version), 16 April 2003, as translated and downloaded from the FBIS Web site on 17 April 2003.

Psychological Operations and the Media

In addition to strategy and tactics, Chinese open source writings paid great attention to the Western media's reporting of events and to the coalition's use of psychological-warfare techniques. PSYWAR is an aspect of Chinese IW just as it is a US IW aspect. Reports focused on propaganda themes, the types of psychological operations used by Western forces, the impact of Western media and its role in the war, and the effect and responsibilities of live media coverage.

It appears that the Chinese vastly overestimated US PSYOP capabilities. For example, on 24 March, it was reported in the Chinese press that the US Defense Department had over 70,000 men engaged in psychological-warfare activities. (US PSYOP commanders wish they had this many soldiers!) The Chinese also believed the US was able to carry out electronic interference against Iraqi news media, to use planes to distribute leaflets, and to use special troops to instigate rebellions among the ranks of Iraqi officers. The US thus opened a second battlefield or front, using rumors and information that combined fact with fiction, which resulted in a soft killing of troops according to the Chinese. In analysis closer to reality, a Chinese reporter noted that six Washington-controlled radio stations were broadcasting news and propaganda programs to Iraq and that US intelligence units were talking to Iraqi senior generals over mobile phones, encouraging them to rebel. Iraqi troops do not have these advantages, he added. More importantly, psychological warfare "is playing an increasingly important role with the arrival of information warfare. The present war against Iraq could mark a turning point in the development of this warfare as it moves from the backstage to the front stage to play a more important role in battle."[359]

When the PRC media commented favorably on one of its own stations reporting on the war, there was a breakthrough of sorts on war coverage in China. Professor Zhan Jiang, director of the Press and Media Department of the China Youth University for Political Science and an expert on wartime media studies, presented his views on China's Iraqi war coverage. He noted that this war was more transparent than that in Afghanistan. Television continued to be the main artery for news coverage, followed by the Internet. Zhan was particularly impressed by two events: first, the fact that there was pluralistic reporting, with Arab TV, the Chinese media, and diversified coverage within the Western media; and second, he was impressed with China Central TV (CCTV), which vastly boosted its public credibility and commercial value by allowing even CNN and FOX pictures to be broadcast. Instead of causing instability in Chinese society, the reporting showed that a new round of reform might be underway in the Chinese media.[360]

---

[359] Tian Zhaoyun and Chen Hui, "Focus on 'Second Battlefield'—How the United States Wages Psychological War against Iraq," <u>Xinhua Domestic Service</u>, 1211 GMT 24 March 2003, as translated and downloaded from the FBIS Web site on 24 March 2003.

[360] Yao Shuo, "War Coverage is In-Depth and Open," <u>Hong Kong Ta Kung Pao</u> (PRC owned newspaper—Internet version), 25 March 2003, as translated and downloaded from the FBIS Web site on 25 March 2003. This is an interview with Zhan Jiang, an expert on wartime media studies who is the director of the Press and Media Department of China Youth University for Political Science.

Chinese reporters also covered what they considered as the propaganda wars between Iraq and Washington. These included the themes of liberation versus invasion, no resistance versus stiff resistance, and the injured or dead Iraqi leadership versus Hussein in full control.[361] One report on 27 March, about the same time that the coalition announced its operational pause, considered just the psychological impact of the war on Americans. It noted that the war had caused a fall in the stock market, that many soldiers had died, that nonmainstream media had enabled people to understand the truth, that US troops had underestimated Hussein, that international opinion had become partial to Iraq, and that if public sentiment for the war waned, the consequences would become worrisome for the administration. The article was filled with Chinese prejudices, such as the point that US soldiers had difficulty getting accurate information since TV programs were "filtered" by the party concerned.[362]

Other Chinese writers stressed how the military and the media in the US spoke with a single voice. Many Chinese reporters focused attention on the embedded reporters, noting that they had become a tool of the military. Information from reporters representing other countries occasionally incurred the wrath of the US government, they added, resulting in the government revoking press privileges. This topic was clearly lacking in objectivity. For example, these Chinese reporters did not mention that US reporters were also removed for stepping outside the lines drawn for them by the Pentagon.

Finally, the Chinese reporters noted that the US was carrying out psychological warfare in the following ways: scattering leaflets; employing media exaggeration to ridicule Hussein and create an aversion to him; threatening and cajoling the Iraqi army to surrender or be punished as war criminals; using repeated exaggerations over the number of surrendering soldiers, the deaths of important leaders, or the fall of certain cities; and destroying Iraq's telephone exchanges and TV stations. News was manipulated by exaggerating US military successes, and the media injected their biases at will. These Chinese writers also felt the Western media had lost its principles of fairness and freedom from following the Pentagon script so closely.[363]

Li Xiguang, director of the Qinghua University International Media Research Center, believed that the war provided a vivid case for media studies. Both sides needed to dominate the media, and they did so by employing the war craft of Master Sun Tzu—for example, "nothing is too deceitful in war" and "making a feint in the east while actually attacking in the west." Li thus demonstrated how stratagems were even imbedded in Chinese analysis of the media. Li noted that the media must reflect the prevailing ideological trend in society at the time war erupts and that society will require reporters to show patriotism and concern for the safety and dignity of US soldiers.

---

[361] Li Bo and Liu Yunfei, "Propaganda War Flares besides Military Confrontation," Xinhua 2153 GMT 26 March 2003, as translated and downloaded from the FBIS Web site on 26 March 2003.
[362] "War Situation Impacts Psychology of Americans," Renmin Ribao (Internet version), 27 March 2003, as translated and downloaded from the FBIS Web site on 27 March 2003
[363] Shi Xiangzhou and Wang Haijing, "What has been Lost by the American News Media?" Liaowang (weekly general affairs journal published by China's official news agency Xinhua), 31 March 2003 No 13, pp. 20-23, as translated and downloaded from the FBIS Web site on 4 April 2003

However, Li believed that the TV networks had only become a microphone for the views of the government and that reporters had created many topics on behalf of the government.[364] Another reporter, also critical of Western media reporting, noted that the media had become a tool to serve the aggressors' psychological-warfare policy thus abusing the purpose of live television. The reporter noted that even if some of the messages were accurate, it was doubtful if they were an overall reflection of the war.[365]

Another reporter suggested that the friendly-fire incidents were part of the US psychological-warfare plan against its own soldiers. The implication was that the Iraqis were successfully fighting the coalition. A way to dampen Iraqi battlefield successes against the coalition was to blame losses on friendly-fire incidents. This in turn would help dampen the psychological impact of the Iraqi army's achievements in the war on US forces and its new recruits. Such "managed" numbers also confuse the opponent.[366] It is interesting to note that while the Chinese analyzed the strengths and weaknesses of the coalition's strategy, tactics, and use of weapons in a rather straightforward way, they appeared to make more mistakes when analyzing the media and psychological-warfare activities.

Finally, a professor of finance, economics, political science, and law provided one of the most interesting and unusual analyses of the paradoxes of the war. The article was interesting because it was a well-written attempt at persuasion that many US analysts should consider as sophisticated PSYWAR material. Author Qiao Xinsheng used Jesus and the Bible on two occasions to support his arguments, along with the words of Abraham Lincoln and Pope John Paul. He stated that the US was using a model to take over countries. This model was to first occupy a country and then form a constitutional government. This happened in Haiti, Panama, Yugoslavia, Afghanistan, and now Iraq, according to Qiao. He added that in an American dictionary there must be a distinction between a good and bad dictatorship, and that constitutions embodying the democratic spirit are not equal to democracy.[367]

Qiao also noted that The New York Times stated the press had become a weapon in this war. Reporters were told not to ask questions concerning US troop casualties, current military actions, and future plans for military actions. To an American such thinking sounds preposterous. No US reporter would expect a commander to expose future plans and current operational activities. Yet Qiao believed this to be yet another example of how the US manipulated the press to serve its interests. US forces allowed only selected disclosure, and then they shifted attention to shirk responsibilities. The

---

[364] Hsu Yung, "War Exposes the Hypocrisy of Press Freedom in the West" and "US News Tags: Pick up a Rock Only to Drop on its Own Feet," Hong Kong Ta Kung Pao, 10, 11 April 2003, p. A10, as translated and downloaded from the FBIS Web site on 11 April 2003.
[365] Lin Zhibo, "How I See Live TV Coverage of the War," Renmin Ribao (Internet version), 4 April 2003, p. 3, as translated and downloaded from the FBIS Web site on 4 April 2003.
[366] Chen Yong, "Insight into the 'Misfires' in the Iraqi War," Xinhua Domestic Service, 0710 GMT 29 March 2003, as translated and downloaded from the FBIS Web site on 29 March 2003.
[367] Qiao Xinsheng, "Six Paradoxes of the Iraq War," Renmin Wang, 4 April 2003, as translated and downloaded from the FBIS Web site on 4 April 2003.

mainstream US media remained shamelessly silent, Qiao added.[368] Again, his analysis reflected that of his compatriots. They believed coalition media sources were absolutely untruthful and manipulative. This is one area in which the Chinese may fool themselves in the years ahead.

Effect on Future Operations

With regard to the effect of the war on future operations, Renmin Wang editor, Li Haiyuan, noted that even though information-warfare, electronic-warfare, and Internet-warfare theories had abounded over the past few years, the real focus of wars is precision-guided strikes which are as important as the development of tanks in the 1930s. These weapons received their marks of importance in the Gulf War and in Kosovo. Today both precision-warfare and urban-warfare theories have taken center stage. These are the areas that demand immediate attention.[369] In another more obscure reference to future operations, it was noted that Chinese analysts gathered much of their information from satellites, and that they must organize satellites that "fly in formation" to fit with future space observation and military requirements.[370]

The Chinese appeared to pay special attention to the 4th Infantry Division, the first fully digitized unit to fight in Iraq. They were especially curious about the capabilities of the division's information-gathering equipment. The Chinese noted that the capabilities of a converted mechanized unit are believed to be three times as great as before digitalization.[371] Former Chinese General Xiong Guangkai added to this assessment, noting that the Iraq War was an extensive test of the fruits of the new US military transformation. "China must maintain a sober understanding of this transformation and earnestly study the new characteristics of partial war under high-tech conditions," he added. In Xiong's opinion, the war reflected the development of smart weapons, the increased use of small military formations, and the systematization of combat forms, integrating sea, air, and land electromagnetism. He was disappointed that the 4th Infantry Division did not see more action because he wanted to study it closely.[372]

The major internal point of concern to the PLA after the war's major battles had ended appeared to be telling the Chinese population that People's War strategy was not affected by the outcome of the fighting in Iraq. This type of warfare, in which the entire population rises up to defend the country against an aggressor, was clearly strained by the

---

[368] Ibid.

[369] Li Haiyuan, "Analysis: Saddam Hoping Urban Warfare will Save Him?" Renmin Wang (Internet version of the People's Daily), 8 April 2003, as translated and downloaded from the FBIS Web site on 8 April 2003.

[370] Hsi Li, "Chinese Satellites Monitor Entire Process of Iraq War," Hong Kong Wen Wei Po (Internet version of PRC owned daily newspaper), 12 April 2003, as translated and downloaded from the FBIS Web site on 12 April 2003.

[371] Chen Hui, "Talk on Iraq War: The Last Battle—US Military Wants to Fight Digitized War," Xinhua Domestic Service, 1251 GMT 13 April 2003, as translated and downloaded from the FBIS Web site on 13 April 2003.

[372] Shi Hongtao, "Xiong Guangkai Talks about Iraq War: China Should Keep Sober Understanding of the World Military Transformation," Qingnian Bao (Internet version of the Communist Youth League daily newspaper), 17 April 2003, as translated and downloaded from the FBIS Web site on 17 April 2003. Xiong Guangkai was a deputy chief of staff and Colonel General in the PLA.

performance of the Iraqi people, who the Chinese believed simply gave up instead of fighting. Chinese theorist Zhang Zhaozhong noted that People's War remained indispensable to China's counterattack operations.[373]

In another article, Zhang went further in his explanation that Iraq did not conduct a true People's War. The characteristics of a People's War, such as the Party's leadership, resolute military units, secure base areas, flexible and mobile strategy and tactics, guerrilla warfare tactics, and the spirit of no fear of death were not present. The Iraqi plan of a war of resistance involving all of the people and concealing the army among the people is certainly not the same as China's plan to conduct People's War. People's War will be indispensable in China's future resistance, self-defense counterattacks, and even in information warfare (where everyone mans a computer). People's War must rely on informationized weapons and equipment, on the national economy, and on the mobilization of all people.[374]

Xiong Guangkai also stated that the war couldn't be called a truly significant People's War.[375] All of this rhetoric about Iraq's failed resistance attempted to distance China's People's War concept from the Iraqi plan. Too many Chinese analysts had tried to template the concept onto Iraqi society, and it simply didn't work. As a result, they were now paying the price for their mistaken analysis and attempting not to lose face.

Zhang noted that the war demonstrated how information war should not only be conducted in the sphere of computer network war but should proceed in coordination with traditional mechanized modes of war.[376] The war allowed the US to observe the entire battlefield, assert real-time control over the battlefield, maneuver rapidly on the battlefield, and strike the Iraqi armed forces with accuracy. Further, the war underscored three areas of future importance: the informationization of weaponry, the development of smaller units with multiple functions and abilities to recombine, and the conduct of joint combat operations.[377]

Strategies and tactics employed by the Iraqis that worked well, according to Zhang, included concealing the military among the people (breaking the whole into parts, thus preserving strength for a protracted war); attacking US military logistical convoys; counterattacking in urban defensive operations in Um Qasr, Basra, and Kut; and concealing the truth and displaying falsehoods, and using underground facilities.[378]

---

[373] Renmin Wang (no further data provided), 15 April 2003, as translated and downloaded from the FBIS Web site on 21 April 2003. Interviews were with PLA National Defense University professors Zhang Zhaozhong and Jin Yinan.

[374] Zhang Zhaozhong, "Thirty Days of the Iraq War," Renmin Wang (Internet version—apparently associated with the People's Daily), 18 April 2003, as translated and downloaded from the FBIS Web site on 18 April 2003.

[375] Shi Hongtao.

[376] Renmin Wang, 15 April 2003.

[377] Zhang Zhaozhong.

[378] Ibid.

Another report on the outcome of the war in Iraq indicated that more countries would now think in terms of preemption since it worked so well for the coalition. This strategy was aided and enabled by the information age. Precision attacks plus the prioritization of psychological operations and other military operations all achieved their objectives to varying degrees. Further the quality of troops was measured as more important than the number of troops. Other countries must focus on building high-tech, quality forces the author Tian Ping concluded.[379]

The China Daily on 28 April stated that the Iraqi War was more influential than previous conflicts for a number of reasons. It was based on the preemptive war theory. It was multi-purposed, in that it was about control over energy resources, and managed to send shockwaves through Asia while maintaining US hegemony. Also the war affected the whole world. The Daily went on to state that major powers would have to adjust their military strategies accordingly. It also added this was the first true information war in human history where information and intelligence played a decisive role and that the war was characterized by an integrated air and ground strategy in which quality conquered quantity. Such successes may encourage Israel, Japan, and Taiwan to act sooner, the Daily added.[380]

Conferences on the War's Conduct and Outcome

China appeared to be quite efficient at quickly organizing conferences to study the outcome of the war in Iraq. On 9 April, it was reported that a symposium on satellite application in the Iraqi War was held two day earlier in Beijing.[381] China's aerospace departments convened the conference. The role of remote sensing satellites in military reconnaissance was stressed in particular. On 8 April at the School of International Studies at Renmin University, a symposium was conducted on the Iraqi War and on international energy security issues.[382]

On 10 April the Hong Kong Singpao Daily News reported that the PLA's four general departments in charge of scientific research institutes, colleges, and schools expanded their analysis of the war in Iraq. While not a "conference" in the formal sense of the word, they requested more media news coverage, satellite monitoring, and daily reports from military attaches in Syria, Turkey, and Jordan. This concentration of effort is greater than any seen in previous wars, according to the report. Other research and analysis was conducted by the Central Military Commission (CMC), the Chief of Staff of the General Staff Department (GSD), and by groups established under the GSD. The CMC reportedly is considering incorporating lessons of the war into its PLA Training Program Guidelines.[383] On 16 April General Xiong Guangkai, Deputy Chief of the PLA

[379] Tian Ping, "Global Military Situation Becoming More Grim," Hong Kong Hsiang Kang Shang Pao (Internet Version of the Hong Kong Commercial Daily, a low circulation paper), 20 April 2003, as translated and downloaded from the FBIS Web site on 21 April 2003. Tian Ping is a special military commentator.
[380] Opinion Page, "War Reshapes Military Landscape," China Daily (Internet Version), 0932 GMT 28 April 2003, as translated and downloaded from the FBIS Web site on 28 April 2003.
[381] China Space News, http://www.china-spacenews.com, 9 April 2003.
[382] Oriental Daily, http://orientaldaily.com.hk, 9 April 2003.
[383] Hong Kong Singpao Daily News, http://www.singpao.com, 10 April 2003.

GSD, said that the war would force military reforms on the PLA. Five points in particular are of interest: the use of intelligent weapons, upgrades of military organizations and structures, the use of automated command and control systems, the multidimensional operational battlefields, and the systemization of operational modes.[384] Finally, on 30 April, leaders of the 2nd Department of the 2nd Research Academy of the China Aerospace Science, Technology and Industry Group (SRA) conducted an intensive study of the coalition's military strategy and operational methods during the war in Iraq. A team of ten experts also analyzed new weapons and equipment. This has resulted in about fifty papers on precision-guided, air defense, and antimissile weapons.[385]

Thus, while it appeared to be a simple task to predict what course of action coalition forces would take in Iraq, reality proved otherwise. The examples of Kosovo and Desert Storm certainly indicated that a massive air assault would be followed quickly by peace or, perhaps, the use of ground forces to conduct a peacekeeping action. However, the course of action settled on at CENTCOM and the adaptations they made along the way (operational pause, reaction to attacks in the rear, etc.) came as a surprise to many observers of US operations, to include the Chinese. The surprise was not limited just to the manner in which the war was conducted (more reliance on ground forces than originally thought) but also with regard to the speed of action and the ease with which objectives were taken. Chinese analysts looked closely at the coalition's use of IW techniques and the effect of IW on future war scenarios. But these were only the initial conclusions that the Chinese drew from the war. The May-August period of analysis, discussed in the next chapter, proved to be a time of even more deep reflection by the PLA. They studied the results of the war closely and tried to apply lessons learned to any potential future conflict.

---

[384] Minpao News, http://full.mingpaonews.com, 17 April 2003.
[385] China Space News, http://www.china-spacenews.com, 30 April 2003.

CHAPTER SEVEN: CHINA'S PERCEPTIONS OF THE BATTLE FOR IRAQ
(MAY-AUGUST 2003)

Introduction

Chinese military analysts continued to examine the activities of coalition forces in Iraq some four months after major hostilities ended. Only after the dust had cleared was a full-scale analysis of events possible. Analysts sought to understand what happened and why, and which strategies, operations, and tactics would or would not work in the future.

The analyses varied. Some articles praised coalition successes and creativity and some did not. Some articles strongly criticized their countrymen for improperly assessing the situation and misinterpreting coalition actions as the war progressed. The open discussion and combination of praise and criticism offers China's military a well-rounded view of the fighting. Which conclusions the PLA's General Staff wishes to draw is another matter, however,

This chapter offers the views of experts and scholars from Chinese military academies developed from May-August 2003. It addresses Chinese views on coalition uses of information warfare techniques and the influence of the revolution in military affairs on coalition operations. It further addresses Chinese observations on psychological operations during the battle for Iraq. Some comments of a general nature are also included in the discussion.

Information War

Major General Wang Baocun, senior IW researcher in the Foreign Military Studies Department of the Academy of Military Sciences, offered his assessment of the coalition's use of IW techniques. He stated that the coalition's use of information technologies and information war was truly impressive. He stressed that the war in Iraq reflected a greater degree of informationization than past wars as seen in the greater effectiveness of command and control, more capable weapons and equipment, and the greater reliance on informationized munitions. He stated that China must work to develop integrated electronic information systems and place greater emphasis on conducting IW exercises both in the field and in combat operations laboratories (simulations). Other requirements included establishing systems integration as a main thread of the revolution in military affairs and developing IW and information technology courses in order to further IW talent in the officer corps. Systems integration includes the development of micro- and macro-information systems as a way to quickly achieve a "critical mass" of information equipment.[386]

In July, staff reporters from Jiefangjun Bao interviewed experts from the Academy of Military Science in Beijing. The focus of the interviews was on the

---

[386] Yang Fan, "People's Liberation Army Rousing Itself to Overtake Others with Major Reforms," Hong Kong Wen Wei Po, 23 August 2003, as translated and downloaded from the FBIS Web site on 23 August 2003.

coalition's use of information war techniques and information technologies during the war. It was noted that "if the Gulf War was a first glimpse at technologically advanced warfare, what was demonstrated by the Iraqi War is an 'information warfare' riptide."[387] Scholar Peng Guanggian stated that the war demonstrated not only a revolution in military technology, but also one in military structures and theory. Theories were tested via simulations. The increase in high-tech military power makes it easier to meet strategic goals by achieving political and economic goals at low risk in an efficient manner.[388]

Scholar Yao Yunzhu gave a tour de force of US military thinking as he demonstrated that, from his point of view, since the 1990s the US has reformed its battlefield theories through "contending thoughts," "identifying concepts," and "developing theories." "Contending thoughts" included a re-look at many of the key concepts of the 1980s: Major General David Deptuala's effects-based operations theory, retired Colonel John Warden's five ring model based on the concept of the enemy as a system, retired Colonel John Boyd's OODA (observe, orient, decide, act) Loop theory, retired Navy officer Harlan Ullman's shock and awe theory, and so on. These new information warfare thoughts replaced the old thoughts of wars of attrition and battles of annihilation.[389] "Identifying concepts" included the elaboration of the Joint Doctrine for 2010 and the Joint Vision for 2020. Finally, Yao identified the Defense Planning Guidance and the 0.5 Version of the White Paper on Rapid and Decisive Combat documents of 1999 as the key links to start the organization and implementation of "developing theories." Yao believe this marked the beginning of the "theory development stage of combat theory innovation of the US military."[390]

In the same interview Wang Baocun stated that the Iraq War demonstrated four US institutional changes: informationized armament system development; innovative theories on wars and operations; the establishment of a mechanism to move from concept, to test, to application; and the development of methods to accelerate the informationization of the military (such as the methods of information dominance, virtual practice, and promotion of the military through the economy).[391] According to Wang, the military information revolution consists of two stages: a military sensor revolution and a military telecom revolution. The first includes the appearance of computer-controlled detectors and the computerization of individual fighting platforms and weaponry systems. This allows the collection of twenty-five times more information than without sensors. The second includes the wide application of digital technology in the military field and the "appearance of systems for directives, control, telecoms, intelligence and computers which are capable of processing a large amount of data."[392] Wang also foresees military informationizing moving from digitalization to Internetization and then robotization. He

---

[387] Li Xuanqing and Chai Yongzhong, "Directly Facing the Roaring Tide of New Institutional Changes of the Military Around the World—Dialogue with Experts and Scholars from the Academy of Military Sciences," Jiefangjun Bao (Liberation Army Daily), 16 July 2003, p. 12, as translated and downloaded from the FBIS Web site on 16 July 2003.
[388] Ibid.
[389] Ibid.
[390] Ibid.
[391] Ibid.
[392] Ibid.

also foresees IW taking place in six dimensions: land, sea, air, outer space, information, and the human psyche. Information and knowledge form the main fighting strength.[393]

Academic Deng Xiaobao discussed the "five watered down distinctions." That is, there will be dwindling distinctions between regional and comprehensive wars; between wars and non-wars (referring here to the lack of distinction between IW and times of peace, where an IW can start with an information assault and the side under attack may not be able to judge that it is a war); between forms of battles that have appeared (for example, Internet-centered battles and electro-Internet integrated battles); between different military branches (which are now more integrated and organized under combat tasks or in accordance with theaters of battle and tasks); and between major and minor participants (for example, nonmilitary professionals such as Internet specialists may become military players). Deng believes that these distinctions indicate that all contending theories and participants will lose their distinctive features.

Finally, scholar Li Xiaodong noted that information factors, to include computation speed, telecom capacity, transmission speed, transmission reliability, ability in real-time reconnaissance and position, and sensibility are the important aspects required to compare strength of the two sides in any future war. By 2010 Li estimates that the percentage of transmitted battle-related data will be 14.5 times greater than in 1992 while speed of transmission will increase five times.

Other experts at the Academy of Military Sciences noted that in the war with Iraq, the "adversary was an asymmetrically weak enemy, and the situation was by no means a classic information war." Analyst Chen Bojiang added that while the war did have characteristics of an information-age war, it was not so in the full sense of the term IW.[394]

The Revolution in Military Affairs

In late May, the Political Bureau of the CPC Central Committee conducted a study session which resulted in Chinese President Hu Jinato offering his first instructions on China's national defense. Hu stressed that the country must "strengthen national defense education, enhance the concept of national defense among all the people, put greater emphasis on developing national defense logistics, and establish and perfect a rapid and effective national defense mobilization system."[395] Xiong Guangkai, deputy chief of the General Staff of the PLA, pointed out:

> The war in Iraq was a further reflection of the development trend toward smarter weapons and equipment, a greater role for aerospace forces, and new developments in missile defense systems. The war reflected the modern requirement for a small staff and structure that is highly trained. Finally the war

---

[393] Ibid.

[394] "A New Milestone for the Revolution in Military Affairs," Shanghai <u>Guoji Zhanwang</u>, 15 June, 2003, pp. 64-69, as translated and downloaded from the FBIS Web site on 15 June 2003.

[395] Kung Shuang-yin, "Beijing Observation: Achieving Development by Leaps and Bounds in National Defense," <u>Hong Kong Ta Kung Pao</u>, 31 May 2003, as translated and downloaded from the FBIS Web site on 31 May 2003.

showed high-tech warfare to be a combination of contact and non-contact combat, in which the trend is toward integrated combat.[396]

The article drew attention to the fact that there are primary components to an "RMA with Chinese characteristics." These characteristics include the fact that information technology mainly involves the vigorous development of computerized weapons and equipment, the energetic promotion of the development of digitized forces, and the vigorous enhancement of the digitized battlefield effort.[397]

Xiong Guangkai, in an earlier article, had offered another name for the revolution in military affairs (RMA), a word change that was not accepted into common usage. He had substituted "military changes" for "military affairs." Xiang felt a deeper understanding of the term and China's domestic situation forced the more precise translation to be "military changes." This designation was prompted by two events: the change in the international situation with the disintegration of the bipolar arrangement, and the emergence of information technology and its influence on military affairs.[398]

Military changes included the following: the intellectualization of weapons and equipment, improvement in quality and reduction in numbers of the armed forces, automated command and control, the multidimensional aspects of fighting space, and the systemization of war—that is, the development of system-to-system joint warfare. Xiong then mentioned that in Iraq all of these factors were present and that China should take these issues under consideration seriously when organizing and planning its force. However, he added that China "should persist in using the method of dialectical analysis and pay attention to viewing issues from an overall view of development." At the same time, he admits that even though information technology is playing the leading role China has not stopped paying attention and warning readers not to negate the role played by people. Xiong, like countless other Chinese writers before him, then stressed the need to carry out mechanization under the guidance of informationization, and promote the latter through the former. He also stressed the need to push forward military changes without discarding the strategies and tactics of People's War.[399]

Major General Ku Guisheng, deputy director of National Defense University, underscored three developments of the RMA. These were military theory (network-centered warfare, informationized warfare, space warfare, etc.), the shape of warfare (real-time command and control, the evolution of technology and equipment and new concept weapons [subsonic-wave weapons, electromagnetic-pulse weapons, laser weapons, weather weapons, and so on]), and adjustments in organization and structure.[400] In another, earlier article, he stated that the change in military affairs (he alternates using RMA and "change in military affairs") would bring four changes to the army: downsizing

---

[396] Ibid.
[397] Ibid.
[398] Xiong Guangkai, "On New Military Changes," Shanghai Jiefang Ribao, 30 May 2003, as translated and downloaded from the FBIS Web site on 30 May 2003.
[399] Ibid.
[400] Ibid.

and rationalizing structure, integrating and modularizing troop composition, making command systems network-based and real-time, and integrating and informationizing support systems.[401]

One journalist in Hong Kong indicated that the Chinese military felt the war in Iraq caused them to think again about the borders and uses of their military theaters/regions. This was because Iraq never brought any of their theaters into play.[402] Shen had recommended this change in his book on Total Information War outlined in Chapter Two. While Iraq designed its theaters based on ground operations, the coalition forces had constructed an information transparent battlefield no longer influenced by geographical boundaries. Tri-service intelligence sharing insured that an "almost completely transparent" battlefield was imaginable.[403] According to one article, some Chinese military experts believe:

> China should establish major military region-level commands which suit China's strategic defense combat operations, and abolish the current military region system demarcated according to traditional areas; that is, change the current system of seven major military regions which are ground force regions arranged primarily by command over an area.[404]

Two changes were deemed required. One was dubbed the "concept of the times" which called for a flat, network-type combat command system. The other was called the "concept of systems" that required resolution of joint command problems. Joint [lianhe] combat operations offer a "kind of equal status and function in an integrated way."[405]

In early August, however, Wenweipo News reported that reorganization of the seven military regions (MR) in China most likely wouldn't happen. It was reported that the MR system is closely "associated with region-based operational strategies/tactics and is well-suited to China's defense policy. That policy promotes military strategy that stresses stable conditions in surrounding countries and active defense...."[406] Instead, MR headquarters will be restructured, and the number of commanders reduced.[407]

General Comments on the Fighting

Opinions varied as to the course and outcome of the fighting in Iraq in the March-April time period, and this tendency prevailed from May to August as well. However, it

---

[401] Ku Guisheng, "The new Change in Military Affairs Calls for the Renewal of the Organizational Setup of China's Military," Liaowang, 28 July 2003, Number 30, pp. 44-46, as translated and downloaded from the FBIS Web site on 28 July 2003.

[402] Yuan Hua, "Pondering the War Between the US and Iraq: Chinese Military Experts Explore Changes in the Theater Command Structure," Hong Kong Tzu Ching, 1 July 2003, Number 153, pp. 58-61, as translated and downloaded from the FBIS Web site on 1 July 2003.

[403] Ibid.

[404] Ibid.

[405] Ibid.

[406] "PLA to Slash 200,000 Troops, Retain Seven Military Regions," Wenweipo News <http://www.wenweipo.com/news.phtml?news_id=CH0308080041%26cat'=002CH, 8 August 2003.

[407] Ibid.

was now easier to see who had correctly and who had incorrectly predicted the course and outcome of the fighting. Articles appeared that criticized Chinese military analysts and military officials. One analyst, for example, wrote in Guofang, the monthly journal of the Academy of Military Science, that Chinese military experts repeatedly made three mistakes: first, they lacked profound research (and thus background for decision making) on the political, economic, and social situation in Iraq, and superficially imposed China's People's War military thinking and strategy of active defense on the Iraqi military; second, they lacked thorough and objective analysis of the strength of the two sides, to include the focused training of the coalition; and third, they lacked sufficient understanding of the impact of the revolution in military affairs, which centered on the use of information technology in modern war and strongly influenced the war's outcome.[408]

In another article, author Yao Jian questioned how military analysts could misjudge the situation so completely. He noted:

> Not only were general viewers not able to understand, but also some military experts frequently made misjudgments in their comments. Results were usually far away from reality, whether it was a prediction of the advance of the US military, or estimates on the Iraqi military's defense, and whether it was quantified analysis or qualified judgment.[409]

Some analysts were punished for their comments. In July CCTV released Zhang from his contract. Zhang was "China's senior military affairs expert" who was idolized publicly by women during the war for his honest and forthright pronouncements and predictions. Zhang is a retired Naval Captain whose analysis of military affairs was held in high esteem in both military and civilian circles in China before the war. What was the reason for his release? He incorrectly forecast almost every coalition action and Iraqi response according to his superiors. He criticized the US for using old tactics and saw the drive on Baghdad as an Iraqi plan to draw the US deep into the city and country. He continued to insist, even after Baghdad fell, that this was all part of a well-conceived Iraqi plan. CCTV listeners felt Zhang had misled them, and some people put him in the same category as other discredited strategists and defeated generals from the Three Kingdoms and Warring States periods. He was also blamed for the great military taboo of "not knowing the enemy and not knowing oneself."[410]

Other analysts offered more measured comments on the course and outcome of the fighting. Zhu Zhenyu, writing for the PLA Daily News, made one of the most interesting comments on the war. He applauded the coalition forces for their flexibility and foresight.

---

[408] Yao Jian, "Why Did Military Experts Repeatedly 'Misjudge'?" Guofang, 15 May 2003, pp. 21-22, as translated and downloaded from the FBIS Web site on 15 May 2003.
[409] Ibid.
[410] Chi Hsiao-hua, "Understanding China," Hong Kong Sing Tao Jih Pao, 28 July 2003, p. A22, as translated and downloaded from the FBIS Web site on 28 July 2003.

Since the Cold War, every time the US has been involved in a war, it almost always adopts different operational theories. The Gulf War of 1991 prominently reflected the focus on the air attack as a "non-linear type mobile war" joint operation theory; in the 1999 Kosovo war, the focus on air attacks reflected an 'asymmetrical,' non-contact joint operation theory. The Afghan war reflected the joint operation theory of 'all out support' of special operations; but in the Iraq war, it put into practice a combined air-ground joint operation theory that focused on the direct attack as a critical element for the rapid seizure of control.[411]

At a meeting of the Academy of Military Sciences experts on 15 June one Chinese analyst also highlighted this US operational flexibility, but in a different way. He noted that the US had discovered that operational capabilities of a joint force, when integrated through information, could be realized to the fullest extent in a war, while the role of numeric superiority in the balance of forces grows continuously more negligible. The war in Iraq was, at least to analyst Yao Yunshu, the first war to make use of this new operational theory. This theory used the characteristics of the information age and symbolized a parting of company with the operational theories of the age of mechanized war.[412] Analyst Luo Yuan added that the operational pattern of the three "not's" (asymmetry, noncontact, non-linear) was utilized. The US Armed Forces used a combination of non-contact and contact operations on the battlefield in which the noncontact aspect was responsible for destroying 70-80% of the enemy's ground defense capabilities.[413]

Luo Yuan, director of the Second Research Office of the Strategic Study Department of the Chinese Academy of Military Science, noted that in the face of such disparity in military capability, there was no hope for Iraq to win. From a political perspective, Luo thought Iraq did better than the US. First, many people viewed the war as illegal. Second, near-term victories aren't long-term victories.[414] For China, Luo felt, the war served as its biggest test of keeping a low strategic profile. The war also improved China's confidence in its ability to resist a high-tech enemy and helped popularize the defense. China must seize, according to Luo, success in the coming twenty-year period of strategic opportunity. To do so it must maintain stability, remember that strategic opportunities are not irreversible, and avoid conflict with the US that is looking at this time period in the same manner.[415]

San Min, an expert in military and national security strategy at China's National Defense University, stated that the US went on the strategic offensive immediately after Afghanistan. San believed that the US analyzed threats in terms of capabilities after Afghanistan, and this was a big change. This led to the formulation of a preemptive

---

[411] Zhu Zhenyu, "Regarding Innovative Operational Theories of the US Forces in the Iraq War, <u>PLA Daily</u> (English edition), 25 June 2003.

[412] "A New Milestone for the Revolution in Military Affairs"

[413] Ibid.

[414] "Thinker's Forum: The US-Iraq War and Postwar Changes in International Relations," <u>Hong Kong Zhongguo Pinglun</u>, 1 May 2003, No 65, pp. 67-77, as downloaded and translated from the FBIS Web site on 1 May 2003.

[415] Ibid.

strategy. The war in Iraq proved to San that a strong core leadership and firm will were needed, that countries must think about times of danger in peacetime, and the right policies and methods must be in place to safeguard strategy and tactics.[416]

Chinese officials also stressed the importance of preparing the nation via mobilization exercises to keep the population in a constant state of readiness. The Mobilization Department of the Shenyang Military Region stressed that the Iraqi War was about strategy, information war, firepower, and competition in the area of mobilizing for war. Mobilization is the foundation for victory, the department noted, and a prerequisite for maintaining the initiative in war. When the military poses requirements, the National Defense Mobilization Commission coordinates, and local governments implement the plan. Legislative work must also be increased. This will ensure the ability to mobilize for People's War, "the magic weapon by which we defeat the enemy and attain victory," and to ensure that victory under high-tech conditions is possible. [417]

The PLA's General Staff stressed that it was necessary to "maintain the traditions of People's War" and announced that the militia would conduct studies on new tactics in the fields of information, psychology, and special warfare. Of crucial importance was "the execution of psychological-warfare training to enhance the militia's special operation capabilities, and studies on new tactics to develop information war by utilizing civilian information technology resources and human resources."[418] Mobilization strategy for the Shenyang Military Region stressed similar requirements. For example, not only must a corps of reserve personnel be developed, but also research on psychological war must be improved. A people's psychological defense awareness is important. Otherwise it will be difficult to convert mobilization potential into real combat power.[419]

Psychological Operations in the Iraqi Conflict

PSYOP lessons were reviewed again in the June-August time period that indicated that the Chinese found much of interest in this area. Chinese analysts stated that the 4th PSYOP Group had distinguished itself in the Gulf War and noted that this time a well-conceived plan was hatched that included three parts: deterrence, mass media, and deception. These plans were launched in spite of two shortcomings according to the Chinese: the war was not just, and it did not have the support of the US population. Other limitations, from a Chinese perspective, included an over-reliance on intelligence, which resulted in misjudging the strategic backdrop against which PSYWAR was conducted.[420]

---

[416] Ibid.

[417] Mobilization Department of the Headquarters of the Shenyang Military Region, "Iraq War Inspires Us to Do Well on National Defense Mobilization Work," Zhongguo Guofang Bao, 12 May 2003, p. 3, as translated and downloaded from the FBIS Web site on 12 May 2003.

[418] "PLA General Staff Department Decides to Step Up Militia Forces in Wake of Iraq War," Xinhua News Agency, http://news.xinhuanet.com/newscenter/2003-05/29/content_891542.htm, 29 May 2003.

[419] Mobilization Department of the Headquarters of the Shenyang Military Region, "Iraq War…."

[420] Wang Xinsheng, Wu Zhizhong, and Luo Xinqin, "Inspirations from Psychological Operations in the Iraq War," Guofang, 15 June 2003, pp. 25-27, as translated and downloaded from the FBIS Web site on 15 June 2003.

US PSYOP focused on six targets from one analyst's perspective. These were the international community, Saddam himself, Saddam's core leadership, senior Iraqi military commanders, ordinary Iraqi officers and men, and the Iraqi public. The US felt it could attack all six targets due to its pre-war PSYOP and control of the mass media. It was believed that if uprisings were staged, the war could be won without firing a shot.[421]

Zhan Jiang and other media-related Chinese professionals explained the impact of the media in a 22 May article. Zhan noted that reporting from the scene made people want to know more about the inside story of the war and was in line with market rules and journalistic principles. Yu Guoming thought the war was an important step for the Chinese media, yet he criticized some media for chasing high audience ratings.

Li Xiguang was upset with Chinese coverage. He noted that much of the media became mouthpieces for CNN. He also thought high audience ratings were sought at the expense of authentic reporting. Zhan, Yu, and Li all looked to TV as the primary medium for reporting. Still newspapers sold well in China, with most people stating that they wanted more news than just TV coverage. It was as if TV were the motivator, and newspapers gave the additional analysis that people wanted. Printed media also corrected mistakes. It was made clear that this was the first time that the Chinese media had reported about a war on such a grandiose scale. At the same time, caution was urged. People were reminded to check two or three sources before believing what they heard. Different media outlets (Western media versus Al-Jazeera, for example) reported vastly different findings.[422] Finally, books did not do as well. The fast pace of the changing operation focused reader attention on late breaking news and not on published accounts of the past. Books just couldn't turn out material fast enough to keep up with the pace of events.

As regards Iraqi propaganda, the Chinese felt they were fairly well prepared this time for defensive propaganda on a strategic scale. They noted that the Iraqis used Al-Jazeera and the Iraqi State TV Station in order to gain public support although they did miss many opportunities as well.[423]

It appears that the Chinese made some mistakes in evaluating the conduct of coalition PSYOP in Iraq. For example, the Chinese felt the US was not as successful this time since it did not understand the Iraqi culture, that it copied Gulf War techniques and methods of operation, that its lies (number of casualties, etc.) were exposed by Iraq, and that it only was prepared to conduct offensive PSYOP and was unable to respond to Iraq's psychological counterattack. In fact, US PSYOP personnel took great care to craft their messages to fit the Iraqi culture. They initially copied the Gulf War approach but changed as the situation changed, and they did not lie about casualties. It is unknown if they were ready to conduct defensive PSYOP but a fair guess is that a backup media plan

[421] Ibid.
[422] Chen Xiang, (no title), <u>Zhongguo Wang</u>, translated by Tang Fuchun for China.org.cn, 22 May 2003, as translated and downloaded from the FBIS Web site on 22 May 2003.
[423] Wang Xinsheng, Wu Zhizhong, and Luo Xinqin .

had been prepared. To US observers, it appears that the Chinese were fooled by their own propaganda and faulty logic.

The overall Chinese assessment of PSYOP was that in high-tech warfare, PSYOP wields tremendous power. Five lessons were highlighted. First, future war should focus on gaining an advantage in PSYWAR by demonstrating that China is fighting a just war. The Chinese indicate that this has always been an important element of their PSYWAR effort. Second, China must improve the ability of its decision makers to improve their PSYOP training and heighten their offensive and defensive awareness in PSYOP. PSYOP can even directly affect the progress and outcome of the war it was noted. Therefore planning to win PSYWAR from a strategic perspective is an important objective. Third, PSYWAR is an important pillar for winning the "information war." China must build up its PSYOP forces at the state and military levels. It is no longer a question of "is it necessary" but "how should it be conducted."[424] At the state level, China must:

- Keep grand strategy in mind in centralizing the guidance and coordination of the state's actions in PSYWAR
- Establish a PSYWAR commission to coordinate the activities of the diplomatic, TV and radio broadcasting, propaganda, and other departments, as well as the PSYOP propaganda activities of the army's departments concerned
- Centralize the leadership, planning, release, and control of wartime news and information in order to insure the unified command and coordination of PSYWAR.[425]

At the army level, China must rely on training professional PSYOP forces and supplement it with work on enemy troops from the masses. This system must include:

- Agencies that organize and direct PSYWAR
- Special PSYOP forces
- Research institutes on PSYWAR
- PSYOP bases
- And reservist PSYOP forces.[426]

Fourth, China's army must set up a propaganda system and reinforce the function of political work in struggling against the enemy. Traditional forms of political work will no longer satisfy the requirements of high-tech war. Military propaganda should include modern mass communications, propaganda, psychology, and behavioral science; pay attention to improving the strategy of propaganda toward foreign countries; attach importance to using advanced information technology and means to more effectively collect and sort out all areas of information concerning its combat opponent; and pay attention to the differences between the target of propaganda and China in terms of ideology, mode of thinking, cultural mentality, national mentality, religious mentality,

---

[424] Ibid.
[425] Ibid.
[426] Ibid.

and other areas; make decisions in a more scientific and objective manner; and use a style and content easily acceptable by the target of propaganda. This helps the Chinese analyst "understand ourselves and the other side."[427]

Finally, China must attach importance to foreign armies' research on PSYWAR and increase the building of PSYOP defense. China must not only study US methods but also intensify research on public mentality, cultural mentality, and on social, political, and economic situations of opponents, and formulate a preparatory plan for PSYOP defense. China also must soberly realize that "PSYOP must be backed up by substantial power and that comprehensive national strength, especially a substantial military power is an important condition for success in PSYWAR."[428] This latter lesson was included in several articles written by Chinese PSYOP specialists over a year before the war in Iraq occurred (see Chapter Five), so it appears to be a lesson that is mentioned over and over by the Chinese.

Also on 15 June at a conference at the Academy of Military Science in Beijing, PSYOP was discussed along with the impact of the revolution in military affairs on conflict and new operational methods employed by the US. Peng Guangqian, a researcher at the Strategic Studies Department of the Academy of Military Sciences, noted that fire strikes were combined with psychological-warfare means in Iraq. These means included secret negotiations with senior military leaders to persuade them to give up resistance before war began; an Internet and cell phone campaign to persuade senior Iraqi officials; the use of TV and thousands of leaflets; the use of CNN, the BBC, and other Western media; and the use of the press conference forum to distribute information. This "deceptive fog of war" helped demoralize the Iraqi soldier and, coupled with the psychological effect of the "shock and awe" firepower display, helped prepare the ground for further PSYOP actions. For example, coalition forces trumpeted the formation of a new government in Iraq, which helped to break down the Iraqi people's psychological defenses, and will to resist.[429]

This latter Chinese report also was full of exaggerations and inaccuracies from a US perspective. It was stated that the US deliberately bombed civilian targets "by mistake" in order to increase the psychological pressure on Iraqi civilians. US forces would not engage in willful actions in contravention of the Geneva Convention, especially with victory so close at hand and against such a weak enemy, as the Chinese have attested. In addition, the small number of such alleged strikes would not affect a nation's will to resist.

Yao Yunzhu, a director of a laboratory in the foreign military department of the Academy of Military Sciences, noted that the US believes a psychological offensive is the best of tactics since it destroys the enemy's will to resist. The use of deception, disinformation, confusion, and leading the enemy astray all led the Iraqi military and society to draw the wrong conclusions about the war and thus induce a top-down collapse

---

[427] Ibid.
[428] Ibid.
[429] "A New Milestone for the Revolution in Military Affairs"

of will. Yao believed the US waged a psychological war on an unprecedented scale and with strength never before seen. It used intimidation, bribery, and the release of false information to achieve their strategic goal of causing the Iraqi will to collapse.[430]

Luo Yuan, director of a laboratory in the Strategic Studies Department of the Academy of Military Sciences, also discussed PSYOP. Luo noted that the speed of the coalition attack was designed to eliminate Hussein's and the Iraqis' will to resist. The idea was to gain a bigger strategic benefit at a lower price—simply the elimination of Hussein. This meant that the US raised PSYWAR to the level of strategy on an unprecedented scale, with unprecedented width, and with an unprecedented multitude of techniques. The emphasis was on "using means that are appropriately powerful, shocking, intimidating, and threatening, in order to induce, force or scare the adversary into accepting the US political goals and the US military objectives."[431]

Finally, a Project Group of the Department of Military Journalism at Nanjing Political Institute wrote a summary report on the media for China Military Science. The FBIS translation of the document only listed "Cai Huifu, et. al." as the authors. They noted that

1. News and public opinion warfare became a "second battlefield" coexisting with the one on which military attacks took place. News and public opinion warfare was played out at the strategic level of war.
2. News and public opinion warfare was highly integrated with psychological warfare and IW. It is necessary to seize psychological superiority through news superiority and information superiority.
3. Being thoroughly familiar with the planning of news and public opinion warfare n wartime is key to knowing the path to victory in news and public opinion warfare.
4. There must be a meticulous setup of topics for discussion.
5. There must be a clever use of truthful speech.
6. It is important to be good at using third parties, and source material must be reshuffled.
7. Make wartime news management more imbued with the characteristics of the times, and implement both "soft" and "hard" measures, both "packaged" and "isolated" measures. Management and control go hand in hand.
8. High-tech news facilities and talented news personnel are key factors in attaining an advantage in news and public opinion warfare.[432]

Conferences

After the fighting ceased in mid-April, the 714th Research Institute held a conference on 24 July. The Institute represented the China State Shipbuilding Industry Corporation. The conference included nineteen experts from various fields of study. The

---

[430] Ibid.
[431] Ibid.
[432] Cai Huifu, et al., "Research into News and Public Opinion Warfare during the Iraq War," Zhongguo Junshi Kexue (China Military Science), 20 August 2003, Number 4, pp. 28-34 as translated and downloaded from the FBIS Web site.

focus of the papers was on the application of strategies and tactics; target selection; strategic sea transport; contributions of the war to the development of China's warship technology; and the use of aircraft carriers, submarines, ship-based aircraft, amphibious ships, precision-guided munitions, UAVs, and Tomahawk cruise missiles. The institute provided information to the State Commission of Science, Technology, and Industry for National Defense (COSTIND) during the war on the transportation implications for China.[433]

Thus after a period of six months, Chinese analysts continued to draw conclusions about the fighting. Some were extremely accurate from a coalition perspective while others were predictably inaccurate. Nevertheless, the Chinese appeared to be learning from the war, especially with regard to the methods and means of deploying and using an information warfare force.

---

[433] "The 714th Research Institute Holds Academic Symposium on the War in Iraq," Naval News, http://anon.free.anonymizer.com/http:/jczs.sina.com.cn/2003-08-13/143425.html, 13 August 2003.

CHAPTER EIGHT: CONCLUSIONS

When examining Chinese IW materials for the past decade, it becomes clear how serious a role IW is playing in the transformation of the PLA from a mechanized to an informationized force. For example, on 6 August 2003 Defense Minister Cao Gangchuan told a meeting of municipal governments, the PLA General Staff, and the Beijing Military Region that the defense buildup was aimed at gaining victory in IW. This IW directed effort also has the complete support of the CMC and its Chairman, Jiang Zemin. Jiang's son Mianheng, by the way, was reported to be the nominee who would serve as an advisor for the 38th Group Army's digitization program. He will be responsible for digitizing weapons and command systems of the unit.

China's leaders believe that the core of the new revolution in military affairs is information operations. IO has changed the structure of combat power by increasing the weight of "soft power." The new transparency, precision, and real-time nature of warfare have changed the traditional forms and methods of combat operations and the principles for directing combat operations (effectiveness, selection of objectives, identifying an operational center of gravity, etc.). Absolute wars are becoming more controllable while local wars more uncontrollable.[434] Most important is the observation:

> Warfare in the era of information requires that strategic and tactical actions be highly flexible. Mechanized warfare upholds the principles of Chinese chess, creating a favorable situation by way of movement. Information warfare abides by the principles of weiqi (also know as Go), constructing a favorable situation by occupying positions…information technology turns a battlefield into a huge, three-dimensional combat operations network.[435]

A review of China's open source literature reveals that China intends to use IW in one of three ways depending on the geopolitical situation confronting its leaders: as a tool of war, as a way to achieve victory without war, or as a means to enhance stability through the promotion of new military theories, such as the information deterrence concept that Shen recommended. The latter use would resemble the nuclear age deterrence concept and other theories that enhanced security and stability during the Cold War. These different methods will present a continual guessing game to the Western mind as it tries to ascertain the actual IW strength of the PLA—is the PLA "appearing weak when strong" or is it trying to "appear strong when weak"?

In the preparation of this book, three primary ideas stood out: China's combined IW emphasis on information control and information supremacy, the use of stratagems in

---

[434] Li Bingyan, "Recognizing One's Own Historical Place in the Flood Tide of Reform: Written on the Conclusion of Discussion of the Topic, 'Is Warfare Gradually Softening'?", Jiefangjun Bao (Liberation Army Daily), 26 December 2000, p. 6, as translated and downloaded from the FBIS Web site on 26 December 2000.

[435] Ibid.

conjunction with IW, and the Chinese focus on psychological operations as a key component of war. All three areas reflect China's history and ancient cultural roots. Additionally, several other issues also stood out in the open source analysis conducted for this work. These issues should carry over into the next ten years of IW development in the PLA. These items are:

1. People's War will play as significant a role, or perhaps more so, in the information age than it did in the nuclear age.
2. Offensive IW has become a subject closely studied by the PLA and is considered an important aspect for the attainment of victory in the information age.
3. IW units will be created.
4. The PLA must establish an advanced officer and NCO development plan so that the PLA can incorporate science and technology into its armed forces.
5. Simulations will continue to play an increasingly important role in the development of the PLA's IW strategy and tactics.
6. In many training exercises a "blue IW-based army" (Western) forces a "red IW-deficient army" (China) to rely on backup systems or the employment of counter tactics which indicates that the PLA expects to absorb a first IW strike.
7. The Second Artillery Corps is the only specified unit the PLA has identified as dedicating attention to IW topics.
8. Future network war and command and control warfare will force the PLA to develop more integrated and joint forces than at any time in its history. Control over information will be as important as information superiority.
9. The wars in Iraq demonstrated to the PLA the power and awe of an information-based force.

All of these items will be briefly discussed below.

People's War and IW

Former Chairman Jiang Zemin noted that no matter what changes occur in the form of warfare, even IW, People's War remains China's magic key to beat any enemy. In the information era, China is laying the material foundation for the armed forces to launch a People's Informationized War. Information resources must be mobilized and specialized forces combined with nonspecialized forces.[436] High technology allows the masses to participate in and support war more easily. The military-civilian compatibility of high technology allows for greater diversity in how masses can take part. People's War is more dependent on the buildup of war energy, is intense and fast paced. The new characteristic is exploiting the country's overall national strength to the maximum extent. New strategies and tactics of People's War should be developed.[437]

---

[436] http://www.pladaily.com.cn/gb/pladaily/2003/04/15/20030415001090_gdyl.html, from FBIS document CPP 20030416000150.
[437] Ren Xiangqun, "High-Technology Conditions and People's Warfare," Zhongguo Guofang Bao, 2 June 2003, p. 3, as translated and downloaded from the FBIS Web site on 2 June 2003.

Taking the Offense in IW

In Chapters One and Three the reserves and regular forces were highlighted as possessing offensive and defensive IW capabilities. Chapter Three focused on the offensive intentions of the PLA, to include possible IW preemption. To demonstrate this emphasis on offensive IW one more time, one need look no further than a third force, the militia. Guangzhou City's militia has, for the past few years, focused on the requirements of the information battlefield. It was decided to organize a battalion headquarters and set up as a provincial telecommunications company and two other companies: a computer network warfare company and an electronic warfare company. The computer network company has two platoons (a network defense platoon and a network attack platoon), and the electronic warfare company has two platoons (one devoted to reconnaissance and the other to deception). However, there is no training outline to follow since this unit is a newly emerging force. A draft Training Plan for Militia Information Technology Elements was developed from discussions with staffs of the Guangzhou Military Region. This year's training research included the topics of protecting one's own network security, searching for enemy network stations, and attacking enemy networks. The report on this unit states that it has successfully achieved noteworthy results in operational methods for launching hacker attacks, propagating viruses, jamming information channels, and disrupting enemy network nodes. NetEase Guangdong (gz.163.com) and the China Unicom Paging Company have already secured arrangements with the unit to provide equipment.[438] Thus even in the militia there is an IW unit that appears to have an offensive mission.

Establishing IW Units

In March 2003 military representatives attending the National People's Congress (NPC) noted that IW units would soon be activated. These units had "already developed electronic jamming/bombardment weapons" capable of paralyzing all enemy electronic systems including the Internet and military command systems, and were more advanced than the US. Several trial units were already established, and a large portion of the budget would go to developing IW units.[439] In May, the journal Liaowang noted "informationization means building information warfare units, then implementing IW. Specifically it means the construction of digitized units." Huo Xiaoyong, a Chinese National Defense University professor, stated that the PLA has organized digitized arms test units on a trial basis.[440] On 4 November 2003 Jiang Zemin, now the Chairman of the Central Military Commission took part in the 15th PLA Military Academies and Colleges Meeting in Beijing. He advocated the promotion of military reforms with Chinese characteristics and asked the armed forces to build IW units to win in IW. New types of soldiers with new military theories are needed to do this, he added.[441]

---

[438] Ye Youcai, Zhou Wenrui, "Building a High-quality Militia Information Technology Element," Guofang, 15 September 2003, p. 45, as translated and downloaded from the FBIS Web site on 15 September 2003.
[439] Mingpao News, 12 March 2003.
[440] China News Agency, http://www.chinanews.com.cn/n/2003-05-20/26/304875.html, 20 May 2003.
[441] The Sun Daily News, http://the-sun.com.hk/channels/news/20031105/20031105012934.html, 5 November 2003.

Increased Emphasis on PSYWAR

The theory of psychological warfare, as noted in Chapter Five, has tremendous significance and value to China. Chinese theorists are attempting to develop an updated ideology and strategy of psychological warfare—one that will focus on intimidation and on exploitation of the differences between Eastern and Western mentalities. The PLA intends to establish a command structure for psychological warfare, as well as create special units that will attempt to overcome Chinese inferiority in high-tech weapons.[442] More important, Chinese theorists appear to believe that because modern psychological warfare can help ensure stability and shape national-security thinking, the concept is more applicable in peace than in war.[443]

In offering a recommendation for future psychological-warfare forces in China, Major General Xu asks Chinese leaders to:

- Develop a psychological-warfare system that integrates specialized and nonspecialized personnel that emphasizes China's special characteristics.
- Establish a psychological-warfare coordination agency at the national level to provide guidance and coordination for national psychological-warfare actions.
- Establish a psychological-warfare command agency under the unified leadership of the Central Military Commission and the party committee.
- Establish several types of psychological-warfare scientific research agencies in order to guide both national and military work.
- Establish a specialized psychological-warfare corps that would form a consolidated and effective psychological attack force.
- Develop a modernized basis for psychological-warfare material and technical equipment.
- Form a people's psychological-warfare mentality by developing psychological-warfare education for the masses and for all commanders in the military.[444]

Other Chinese analysts believe China has many psychological-warfare shortcomings to overcome. These include the backwardness and non-specialization of current Chinese psychological-operations forces, a lack of talent, and the difficulty of forming a unified and coordinated psychological-warfare command. China lacks a unified understanding of the strategic role of psychological warfare and of the role that psychological warfare can play in high-tech local wars.[445] Still other analysts believe that in order for China to overcome its weakness in equipment, materials, and technical content, it must develop a force that combines its mass-action strength with a specialized

---

[442] Ibid.
[443] Xu Hezhen, "Focus on Psychological War Against the Background of Grand Strategy," Zhongguo Junshi Kexue (China Military Science), Number 5 2000, pp. 67-76, as translated and downloaded from the FBIS Web site on 11 December 2000.
[444] Ibid.
[445] Wang Zhenxing and Yang Suping, "On PSYWAR in Recent High-Tech Local wars," Zhongguo Junshi Kexue (China Military Science), 20 December 2000, pp. 127-133, as translated and downloaded from the FBIS Web site on 8 March 2001.

structure for psychological warfare.[446] Overall, these shortcomings hurt the development of a coordinated psychological-warfare strategy for the PLA.

Finally, China will continue to view the US as its major psychological-warfare threat. Xu says that the US objective is to gain benefits from the Chinese consumer market and to maintain long-term political and psychological pressure on China. The US will accomplish that objective by attacking China's national self-respect and by compelling China to do what the US asks.[447] Xu warns the Chinese that psychological acceptance of socialism depends on China's comprehensive national strength and on the level of progress that the social system achieves in economic development and in socialist awakening. He says that one cannot believe that "the foreign moon is rounder than our own," for this is defeatist psychology (the moon is a reference to a Chinese phrase from the early 1900s that advocated "total Westernization"). Conviction in the correctness of one's own system is what works, and that is what is required.[448] This focus is not just on reserve or PLA use of PSYWAR. It was reported on 20 June that the militia had established its first PSYWAR element in the People's Armored Forces Department of Jiujiang County, Jiangxi Province. The element also conducted its first exercise as well.[449]

In the end, we should not expect China to waver from the main characteristics of its psychological-warfare doctrine: strong reliance on the use of war experience, deep cultural roots, the influence of Marxist materialist dialectics, and the role of strategic deception.[450] China will use power projection as a means of achieving success in influencing the activities of foreign nations. Its centralized leadership system will continue to exert control over the news, propaganda, and public opinion.[451] Most important for Western analysts is the fact that Chinese theorists "think" strategically in a way that few foreigners do. Western analysts will have to come to terms with this fact if they are to learn to predict Chinese psychological-warfare strategy in the coming years.

Training the Officer and NCO Corps

China's Central Military Commission issued a Plan for Implementing the Military Personnel Strategy Project in September. The plan included a strategy to "suit the changes in the forms of war." It was noted that there is a need to build an informationized army and win informationized wars. This will require a number, knowledge structure, and quality of military personnel in the next ten to twenty years that does not exist at the

---

[446] Wang Lianshui, Ma Jingcheng and Yan Jianhong, "Comparison of Psychological Warfare between China and the West," Zhongguo Junshi Kexue (China Military Science), Number 6 2000, pp. 102-110, as translated and downloaded from the FBIS Web site on 25 June 2001.
[447] Xu Hezhen, "Focus on Psychological War."
[448] Ibid.
[449] China Defense News,
http://www.pladaily.com.cn/gb/defence/2003/07/24/20030724017045_mbyby.html, 24 July 2003.
[450] Wu Juncang and Zhang Qiancheng, "The Doctrine of Psychological Operations in Ancient China," Zhongguo Junshi Kexue (China Military Science), Number 5 2002, pp. 88-94, as translated and downloaded from the FBIS Web site on 14 January 2002.
[451] Wang Lianshui, Ma Jingcheng and Yan Jianhong.

present. Officers, scientists, technical experts, and noncommissioned officers are needed to make the plan work.[452]

As an example of how the plan is being implemented, in November 2003 an inspection was conducted at the Guangzhou Military Command on thirteen IW training subjects. The successful result of the inspection was due to the new Outline of Military Training and Evaluation that listed IW training requirements, according to the article explaining the inspection. The division established ten training databases for an armored corps, communication corps, artillery corps, and a reconnaissance force, and it prepared over three hundred online simulation drill subjects. Confrontation simulation exercises were conducted which included "network information offensive and defensive exercises, counterattacking computer viruses, reconnaissance and counterreconnaissance, electromagnetism interference and anti-interference, 'soft strike and hard strike,' and psychological-warfare" training aimed at boosting officers' IW capabilities as well as the ability to work out strategy and tactics in close-to-real combat IW environments.[453] If this is true, then some Chinese units are off to a good start with their training.

Further, the Dalian Warship Institute noted in a PLA Daily article that 96% of the theses done by the 2003 graduating class were on new theories of information warfare. That is, the Institute has cultivated a number of experts in IW for the Navy. Such training ensures that officers are keeping in step with developments in information technology.[454]

Simulations and Training Exercises

There were numerous simulations developed and run during the exercises that were listed in Chapter Three. These were developed in order to speed the informationization process. In addition, the following virtual platform training facilities were discussed in other PLA articles in 2003.

20 January—Naval Command College offers special training on foreign military campaign theories, command of campaigns and operations, and naval IW. Students use naval warfare laboratories and specialized subject classrooms to conduct computer-simulated warfare.[455]

11 March—The Second Artillery Corps has built network-based military training platforms. Here the corps conducts network-based and simulated military exercises with

---

[452] Zhong Jing, "To Build Five Contingents of Commanding Officers, Staff Officers, Scientists, Technical Experts, and Noncommissioned Officers and Train Military Personnel for Informatized Warfare, Chinese Military Implements Personnel Strategy Project," Liaowang, 29 September 2003, pp. 50-51, as translated and downloaded from the FBIS Web site on 29 September 2003.

[453] Huang Jicheng and Peng Zecheng, "Division Explores New Training Methods for IW," Jiefangjun Bao (Liberation Army Daily) (Internet version), 28 November 2003, from FBIS report CPP20031202000086.

[454] http://www.pladaily.com.cn/gb/pladaily/2003/07/26/20030726001025, from FBIS document CPP 20030811000030.

[455] 20 January 2003, http://www.pladaily.com, from FBIS document CPP20030203000055.

IT. Commanders can observe and analyze simulated operations between "red" and "blue" armies.[456]

3 April—Logistics organs in the Tibet Military District have set up network-based information platforms.[457]

28 June—The PLA Artillery Corps Command Academy has developed a system for virtual reality firing of short-range cannons of a "certain model" in its Hong Kong Garrison. The system is planned for integration into other artillery corps over the next few years.[458]

21 July—A Hebei Reserve Artillery Division has invested 14 million yuan in an informationized training platform composed of an information battle room, tactics operation room, and professional training simulation room. Online drilling is available for eight hundred people. Information devices are also integrated into a transportation truck to become a political work and psychological-warfare vehicle "integrated with PSYWAR maneuver, audio/video production, cable TV meeting and other fighting capacities." A couple of PCs connected with field operations automatic command systems can carry out network offensive and defensive battles.[459]

21 August—The Navy Submarine Academy conducted maneuvers using a newly developed submarine tactical simulated training system.[460]

16 September—During a training exercise in Guangzhou, it was noted that one division had "invested over 100,000 RMB to construct a training ground for simulated psychological warfare." The description of PSYWAR indicated that the simulation would help Chinese soldiers withstand the horrors of war.[461]

27 September—A software training class on vehicle and ship maintenance equipment and materials management systems was held in the Shenyang Military Region. A complete set of computer network equipment and software was distributed to subordinate units. One unit then came up with an idea of how to build an information platform for vehicle and ship maintenance.[462]

29 October—On 17 October, the PLA's first online simulated training system for psychological-warfare training developed by the PLA Nanjing Political Institute passed the critical evaluation of experts. The system is made up of three subsystems including

---

[456] http://www.pladaily.com.cn/gb/pladaily/2003/03/12/20030312001157_Army.html, from FBIS document CPP20030313000039.

[457] http://www.pladaily.com.cn/gb/pladaily/2003/01/28/2003/04/03/20030403001010_TodayNews.html, from FBIS document CPP20030409000119.

[458] http://www.takungpao.com/inc/print_me.asp?url=/news/2003-06-28/GW-149434.htm&date=2003-6, from FBIS document CPP20030716000017.

[459] Li Yonglong and Li Jianzhou, "IT Application Pushes Online Drilling," Jiefangjun Bao (Liberation Army Daily) (Internet version), 21 July 2003, as translated and downloaded from the FBIS Web site on 21 July 2003.

[460] http://www.pladaily.com.cn/gb/pladaily/2003/08/21/20030821001020_Army.html, from FBIS document CPP20030821000146.

[461] Zeng Bin, Zhou Shiqiang, Liu Changshan, Wu Zhifan, and Sun Bingxiang, "Sword Coming Out of the Scabbard and Shows its Sharpness," Guangzhou Zhanshi Bao, 16 September 2003, p. 2, as translated and downloaded from the FBIS Web site on 16 September 2003.

[462] Yang Guang and Li Yunbo, "Information Platform for Maintenance Equipment and Materials Management Developed," Jiefangjun Bao (Liberation Army Daily) (Internet version), 27 September 2003, as translated and downloaded from the FBIS Web site on 27 September 2003.

the Education and Training System for Psychological Warfare. The system is part of the reform effort to realize the simulation and online training of the military.[463]
31 October—A submarine virtual training center was formally put to use by the Submarine Institute of the PLA.[464]
11 November—In mid-October at the Informationized Simulation Combat Command Training Center of an armored brigade in the Beijing Military Region, an informationized simulation confrontation was held that integrated soft killing with hard strike. The brigade allocated funds to build the center that integrates the training of electronic warfare, network warfare, and psychological war. The brigade also intensified its effort to cultivate commanders' knowledge of IW theory and included psychological warfare and electronic warfare in the training plan.[465]

"Blue" versus "Red"

There were numerous training exercises in which a "blue IW- based army" force confronted a "red IW-deficient army." In the ensuing battle, the red force had to rely on backup systems or the employment of countertactics. In nearly every instance these counters included counterreconnaissance and counterinterference. The impression left with the reader is that the PLA expects to absorb a first IW strike like a fighter on the ropes, and then counter after the opponent has taken his best shot.

One of the most extensive write-ups of an exercise occurred in September in Guangdong Province. A short synopsis of the exercise follows which demonstrates the red versus blue factor as well as a host of other elements discussed above:

A mammoth verification-type exercise was conducted here in the first part of September. Electromagnetic jamming, satellite communications, executing psychological warfare—all sorts of combat situations which could arise at any time on a future battlefield were explored. The key lies to adapting to changing circumstances. The setting of the exercise was a joint amphibious landing campaign under high-tech conditions. The unit operated for seven continuous days and nights, a distance of nearly 1000 km and with a sea crossing of nearly 100 nautical miles. In high-tech war, sea, land, air, space, and the electromagnetic spectrum emerge as one. There is a high degree of integration and the emphasis is on the information confrontation. Red force electronic jamming elements change frequency from time to time as they emit continuous electronic jamming aimed at the enemy. Hackers on line, electronic bombs, and pulse bombs sporadically attack the enemy force's command networks. The enemy's command systems are seriously disrupted, and command is repeatedly interrupted and rendered ineffective. Special operations troops aboard powered delta-wing aircraft come flying in like supernatural warriors dropping from the heavens and skimming the sea.

---

[463] "Nanjing Political Institute has a Simulated System for Psychological Training," PLA Daily in English, 29 October 2003.
[464] http://English.pladaily.com.cn/English/pladaily/2003/10/31/20031031001016_MilitaryNews.html, 31 October 2003.
[465] Hou Mingjun and Liu Yongbin, "Simulation-training Platform Built to Boost Information Combat Capacity," Jiefangjun Bao (Liberation Army Daily), 11 November 2003, as translated and downloaded from the FBIS Web site on 11 November 2003.

After landing craft hit the beach, psychological-warfare propaganda vehicles charged ashore and went into battle. They called out to the enemy using various languages, and huge balloons burst above the lines to scatter leaflets. UAVs dropped letters from family members on enemy officers. Naval artillery fired propaganda shells from time to time. Computer network psychological warfare was conducted, sending information and cartoons to clog up the enemy's command net and propaganda net. The training the "red" unit conducted has greatly strengthened the unit's battlefield adaptability, its psychological attack ability, and its psychological defense ability. New equipment such as backpack loudspeakers and armored propaganda vehicles also help.[466]

The Second Artillery Corps

China's strategic nuclear forces, also known as the Second Artillery Corps, apparently have been the focus of a major IW effort. Interestingly, this Corps is the only unit that the PLA specified as training and exercising extensively with IW. More wasn't added to the description of PLA exercises because the majority of articles about the Second Artillery Corps did not specify in which region the exercises were held.

The Second Artillery Corps's Engineering Academy, called the cradle of strategic missile experts, has not only been equipped with electronic systems but also with network servers for teaching and lecturing, and it has added a course on psychology.[467] The psychology course is required and is designed to enhance the unit's psychological capacities. Further, the Corps took part in a psychological-warfare drill under future warfare conditions. Since the Corps will take on special missions in future war, it has set strict demands on its officers' and mens' psychological qualities. A good psychological state enhances operational strength, it is believed.[468]

In addition to the two exercises on the Second Artillery noted in Chapter Three's listing of IW exercises by region, there are a host of other reports about the Second Artillery Corps that are worth following. For example, there are reports that the Second Artillery Corps has a digitized barrack (most likely for a headquarters, not troops) with an integrated automated command network, satellite broadband network (SBN), LAN, audio-visual instruction network, and broadcast television network. It can thus conduct teleconferences and digital audio-visual training. The Second Artillery Research Institute reportedly has sent its people out to universities to get advanced degrees in order to accomplish the "historical task of informationization of the Chinese army." A Second Artillery Brigade has established a data exchange platform with unified standards for the whole brigade and has extended its application of the information network into operations, training, and management fields. Technicians have developed an intelligent management system that updates system contents regularly to ensure the availability of real-time information.

---

[466] Zeng Bin, Zhou Shiqiang, Liu Changshan, Wu Zhifan, and Sun Bingxiang.
[467] http://zqb.cyol.com/gb/zqb/2003-11/20/content_774893.thm, from FBIS document CPP 20031204000020.
[468] http://www.pladaily.com.cn/gb/defense/2003/11/24/20031124001009_TodayNews.html, from FBIS document CPP 20031204000020.

Joint Forces

From the discussion above, it is evident that reserve, militia, PLA, and civilian forces will conduct joint operations in the future and join hands against any intervening IW force. This integration is already underway, as signified by the proposed establishment of a cyber-security force. Qu Yanwen, a security specialist, has proposed that a cyber-security force (CSF) be composed of members of the PLA, the Ministries of State Security and Public Security, and technical specialists. Currently Chinese political, economic, and military security is in danger due to the nascent stage of development of China's networks. Weaknesses exist in financial security, in defending against cyber attacks against information networks of key organizations and computer-based fund raising operations and scams, in information control over data that can affect the stability of public order, and in military information security.[469] Within the PLA, the Shijiazhuang Army Command College, the Navy Command Academy, the Air Force Command Academy, and the Second Artillery Corps Command Academy met in July to work out an overall joint teaching program for the three armed forces. They are trying to share information resources and exchange experiences via the Internet, among other issues.[470]

Lessons Learned from Iraq

In Iraq, the Chinese witnessed first-hand the power and awe of an informationized force. In summing up his arguments on the war during a session at the Academy of Military Sciences, IW expert Wang Baocun noted the following as the future needs of the PLA:

> We should regard 'benefits for the rapid exchange and use of information' as the objective, reform the system for leadership and directives, reform the military establishment, flatten the directive pattern, join military forces of different branches into one unit, and establish a structure of military forces that meets the requirements of winning high-tech wars and information-based warfare...we should highlight training on 'information-based battles,' provide courses related to information-based battles and information technology, and cultivate as many as possible highly qualified military professionals and professional military officers who are experts in computer systems and the Internet and information technology.[471]

The Chinese military viewed with great interest how Western militaries adapted information technology to their equipment and to their strategy and tactics. Their impressions from this study, from events in Iraq in 1991 and 2003, and from domestic

---

[469] Takungpao News, http:www.takungpao.com/news/2003-11-30/MW-203198.htm, Naval News http:jczs.sina.com.cn/2003-11-30/167226.thml, 30 November 2003.
[470] http:www.pladaily.com.cn/gb/pladaily/2003/07/31/20030731001027, from FBIS document CPP 20030811000030.
[471] Li Xuanqing, Chai Yongzhong, and Bao Guojun, "Directly Facing the Roaring Tide of New Institutional Changes of the Military around the World—Dialogue with Experts and Scholars from the Academy of Military Sciences" (Internet version), 16 July 2003, p. 12, as translated and downloaded from the FBIS Web site on 16 July 2003.

events such as the recent launch of a man into outer space, have influenced the Chinese approach to military reform. They write extensively about capturing information technology in the reform process at every opportunity.

FBIS Translation Support

Immediately after the fall of the Soviet Union, the most important military journal of the Soviet armed forces that survived the move to the Russian armed forces, <u>Military Thought</u>, was translated in its entirety. Today, for different reasons, <u>China Military Science</u> should receive the same treatment. It is very important to understand Chinese thinking at this crucial time in the history of the US and China and to avert bloodshed at any cost. A better understanding of the concerns, problems, and strengths of the PLA may help prevent potential future misunderstandings. <u>China Military Science</u> has a multitude of articles that should be read and understood by Western analysts. The topics include strategy, new training techniques, joint operations, campaign development, combat power measurement, new weapons, political work in the army, the use of Sun Tzu military theory in the contemporary world, the influence of science and technology on strategy, the military's view on Taiwan, and military culture.

In conclusion, Chinese military theorists apparently believe they have found a willing, relatively cheap, and malleable ally in IW, an ally that can enable China to catch up with the West in both strategic military and international status. These areas could lead China to play an important strategic deterrent role (or potential troublemaker) in the Asia-Pacific region in the future and to gradually emerge into an economic competitor worthy of close scrutiny. China sees a strategic opportunity to leap frog the age of mechanization and move directly into the age of information, a move full of positive aspects for the Chinese military.

China's IW emphasis still reflects a mixture of Western and Chinese thinking, but it is moving away from the former. As mentioned earlier, there are fewer definitions of IW today than in the mid-to-late 90s. But there have been significant developments in the characteristics of Chinese IW, characteristics that differ significantly from those of the US. Those US planners working on counter IW strategies should take these differences into consideration. The US spends far too little time on stratagems, for example, and must think about countering electronic strategies.

Thus, for the US military, a force which is focused on information superiority, dominant maneuver, digitalization, and information assurance, a study of Chinese IW methods would be not only advisable but should be required. Such a study might uncover inherent IW weaknesses in the US system when analyzed through the thought process of another ideological prism or framework. At a bare minimum it would provoke thoughts on how to counter a force using such tactics and thinking, whether it be China or some other nation. The absolute worst mistake that America can make is to use its own process for uncovering vulnerabilities exclusively since there are other problem-solving schemes (the dialectic) available. As the Chinese have said, losers in IW will not just be those with backward technology, they will also be those who lack command thinking and the ability to apply strategies.

China, for its part, has been able to learn from studying IW theory in other countries. This has allowed the PLA to avoid some of the mistakes of others and to pick out the best elements in these theories. As a result, China may become an IW force with which to reckon. IW has allowed China to skip over some technological developments, and to use discoveries in the West to "borrow a ladder to climb the tree."[472]

It is a Chinese proclivity to stress control, strategies, People's War, and other Chinese characteristics of their historical military thinking instead of just relying on information superiority and "system of systems" theories that have become the norm in the West. In many ways, Chinese thinking is closer to that of the Russians due to a common frame of reference (military art and the Marxist dialectic). There has also evolved a specific Chinese IW lexicon that is different from Russian and Western terminologies. It includes such terms as acupuncture warfare, military soft science,[473] and an informationized army.

A listing of some, but not all, of the important new topics covered in this book includes the concept of integrated network-electronic warfare (INEW); the creation of new information warfare institutes that will serve as "aircraft carriers" of science and technology; the renewed focus on integrating technology with the ancient Chinese concept of stratagems, an asymmetric approach to warfare; and the more worrisome development of IW units ready to implement "active offensive" activities. The really rich Chinese IW concepts are more likely than not buried away in their rules and regulations within the General Staff Directorates and research institutes. China's IW rules and regulations are not available to other nations—a vast difference from unclassified US doctrine that is available to anyone on the Internet. In addition to keeping their manuals close to their chest, China's censors also still refuse to divulge the actual name or number of units. The use of such methods will continue to keep Chinese military thinking wrapped in a blanket of secrecy.

Electrons and information technologies are the new formations of the 21st century armed forces of China and other countries that supplement traditional forces. Electrons require that the focus or concentration of effort be on operational effectiveness instead of the principle of concentrating military strength. A core issue will be the fight for network supremacy. It will be necessary simultaneously to win in strategy by winning in battle. Further, electrons may be used as strategies to fool network operators or to destroy networks. During several exercises it was noted that "electron deception" or "electron feints" were employed, for example. As a result, clouds of electrons may be able to disable and destroy countries (usually via economic destruction, but also via information-psychological attacks) where large armies once were required. The West should look to

---

[472] Wang Jianghuai and Lin Dong, "Viewing Our Army's Quality Building from the Perspective of What Information Warfare Demands," Beijing Jiefangjun Bao (Liberation Army Daily), 3 March 1998, p. 6, as translated and downloaded from the FBIS Web site on 16 March 1998.
[473] Shen Weiguang, "Focus of Contemporary World Military Revolution—Introduction to research in IW."

the East for explanations of these stratagems for, as the Chinese note, they allow more time for strategic thinking than their Occidental counterparts. A few new areas of emphasis support these strategies. They include the new criteria for figuring correlation of forces and the new emphasis on cognitive factors, especially psychological.

Building systems of soft destruction (signal deception or interference) will become as important as firepower. Chinese analysts believe operations are switching from firepower to detecting, concealing, searching, and avoiding, which allows long range combat to replace hand to hand fighting.

Of greatest immediate concern to US policy makers, however, is the material in the book on strategy from the Chinese National Defense University that indicates China might be thinking of conducting a "war of annihilation" or preemption strategy against enemy networks. If China feels it can only gain the initiative and information superiority by preemptive strikes, then the coming years may witness some uneasy times, and China may be more of a threat than the introduction to this book contends. It was easy to measure the intent of steel in the form of a tank. It will be much more difficult to measure the intent of an electron and to conduct the consequence management actions that accompany electronic attempts to deceive high-tech systems or that attempt to force errors in the cognitive processes of decision-makers.

Hopefully, all countries engaged in the development of IW forces will learn to talk and negotiate with one another, perhaps through the establishment of an IW hotline between governments. Since it will be more difficult to know who or what is attacking a nation in the age of information, such devices will become even more important and vital to our national security than they were in the past. Everyone world-wide will know if a nuclear device is detonated but not everyone will know if an electronic attack on, say, a nuclear station is launched. In the information age it is possible to mask attacks and make them appear to come from someplace other than the originator of the attack. The hotline will enable clarifications of attack status, and it would allow nations to correspond and sort out what has happened, thereby reducing misunderstanding over a very serious issue. In fact, such a hotline could be collocated with the current nuclear hotline. Without such devices, we are inviting not only misunderstanding, but also horrible problems with unknown consequences. Neither the Chinese nor the West is interested in such scenarios.

APPENDIX ONE: IW ARTICLES IN <u>CHINA MILITARY SCIENCE</u>: 1999-2003

The titles listed in English below are from the journal <u>China Military Science</u> and are representative of the IW content of this PLA journal. However, all PLA journals are writing extensively on the subject. The journal <u>National Defense</u>, for example, had nearly twenty-five articles on "information mobilization" in 2003.[474] The <u>Liberation Army Daily</u> also wrote extensively on the subject of IW.

The titles in this section are listed as they appeared in <u>China Military Science</u>, starting with the most current issue available and working backward to the first issue in 1999. The listing demonstrates how studiously the PLA is covering the IW aspect of future war.

Only those titles with "high-tech," "digitalization," "precision," "network," or "information" in the title are listed. Any Chinese discussion of US IO is also listed. There are numerous other articles and themes that include the topic of IO and IW (military reform, innovations in military thinking, psychological operations, asymmetry, strategy, talent training, nanotechnology, space, operations, revolution in military affairs, etc.) that are not included in the list below. One exception was made—Wang Baocun's article on the RMA that only covered information topics.

Number 6, 2003
"On the Logistic Informationization of the PLA," Nie Hexing, pp. 120-126.
"Analysis of the Mobilization of the National Economy under the Conditions of Informationization," Zhu Qinglin, pp. 127-132.

Number 5, 2003
"Deliberation on the Strategy of the Development of the Land Force's Mechanization and Informationization," Chen Yong, pp. 101-109.
"The Status Quo and Trends of Development of the Informationization of the US Armed Forces," pp. 148-154.

Number 4, 2003
"Characteristics of Sun Tzu's Simple Information Thinking," Wang Shuomin, pp. 70-74.
"Development in Military High-Tech and Update of Military Strategic Thinking," Li Deyi, pp. 87-93.

Number 3, 2003
"Information Frontier Defense: Prospect of Future Frontier Defense," Xu Peilie and Zhang Shengjiang, pp. 37-39.
"Study of Jiang Zeming's Thinking of Army Informationization," Xu Jinyu, pp. 49-52.

---

[474] The author would like to thank Mr. John Tai for examining the 2003 issues of <u>National Defense</u> and uncovering this fact.

"Develop Army Informationization with Deepening Cognition and Scientific Guidance," Zhu Qi, pp. 86-90.
"Summary of the Studies of the Theory of Information Operations," Xia Zhengnan, pp. 151-156.

Number 2, 2003
"On Seizing Information Supremacy," Dai Qingmin, pp. 9-17.
"Basic Features and Trend of Development of Informationization War," Zhang Bisheng, pp. 63-72.
"Rational Consideration on Army Information Construction," Sun Haicheng, Liu Hanming, and Ji Shidong, pp. 73-80.
"Studies in Guiding Ideology of Information Operations in Joint Campaign," Ke Zhansan, pp. 81-84.

Number 1, 2003
"High-Tech Warfare and Transformation of Military Thinking Methods," Yan Gaohong and Zhang Xueming, pp. 99-105.

Number 6, 2002
"Deliberation of the Principles of Information War," Zeng Qingyang, pp. 55-60.
"On Modern High-Tech Wars and the Law of War," Zhao Xiaodong, pp. 61-65.
"On Development of Army Informationization and Information Warfare," Dai Qingmin, pp. 66-70.
"On Precise Warfare," Li Daguang, pp. 97-102.

Number 5, 2002
"US Army Preparations for Future War: Network Centric Warfare," Wang Baocun, pp. 133-143.

Number 4, 2002
"Digitalization: A Profound Reform in Contemporary Military Culture," Shen Guangqin and Jiang Defu, pp. 71-77.
"Rationally Understand the Human Factors in High-Tech Wars," Yang Chunchang and Ren Zhenjie, pp. 135-141.

Number 3, 2002
"Views on Construction of Transportation Battlefields in High-Tech Wars," Yao Youzhi and Chen Zeliang, pp. 56-63.
"Views on the Theory of Dominant Operations—On Domination of Information and Traffic," Wang Xingwang, pp. 129-132.

Number 2, 2002
"Strategic Conception of Mechanization Development Guided by Information," Xu Xiaoyan, pp. 107-111.
"On Integrating Network Warfare and Electronic Warfare," Dai Qingmin, pp. 112-117.
"Elaboration on the Theory of Information Warfare," Zhang Zhanjun, pp. 118-124.

Number 1, 2002
"From Mechanized Military Affairs to Informationized Military Affairs: The Transformation of Military Paradigms Across the Era," Wang Baocun, pp. 102-109.
"Debate on the So-called 'Essential Character of Nonviolence' of Information Warfare," Wang Pufeng, pp. 124-126.

Number 6, 2001
"The Emergence of High-Tech War and its Position in History," Feng Haiming and Xiong Yuxiang, pp. 35-42.
"Developing the Spiritual Motivations of the Members of the Armed Forces Under the Conditions of High-Tech War," Xiao Yichao and He Xiaozhou, pp. 105-109.

Number 5, 2001
"China and the Revolution in Military Affairs (2)," Wang Baocun, pp. 149-156.

Number 4, 2001
"China and the Revolution in Military Affairs (1)," Wang Baocun, pp. 147-154.

Number 3, 2001
"The Characteristics of Informationized War," Liu Aimin, pp. 69-72.
"Understanding the Fundamentals Affecting the Outcome of High-Tech Local Wars," Liang Biqin and Sun Jianxiang, p. 149.

Number 2, 2001
"Realize the Leap-Forward Development of the Army through Mechanization Driven by Informationization," He Jiasheng, pp. 121-127.

Number 1, 2001
"Main Issues of Defense of Logistics in Regional Wars under High-Tech Conditions," Xu Yong, Li Renfu, and Ma Luan, pp. 74-80.
"Revolution in Information Technology and Creation in Command Theory," Lin Dong, Wang Jianghuai, and Chen Taiyi, pp. 90-100.

Number 6, 2000
"On Psychological Warfare in Recent High-Tech Local Wars," Wang Zhengxing and Yang Suping, pp. 127-132.
"Science and Technology: The First Decisive Factor in High-Tech Local Wars," Guo Dafang, pp. 144-148.

Number 5, 2000
"Establishing the Information-Resource Mobilization Mechanism with Chinese Characteristics," Xu Xiaoyan, pp. 77-82.
"New Changes in War Economic Mobilization in High-Tech Conditions," Xing Jianhua, pp. 113-116.
"Building Information Defense to Safeguard National Security," Yang Shisong, p. 151.

Number 4, 2000
"Innovating and Developing Views of Information Operations," Dai Qingmin, pp. 72-77.
"Planning and Application of Strategies of Information Operations in High-Tech Local War," Niu Li, Li Jiangzhou, and Xu Dehui, pp. 115-122.

Number 3, 2000
"Development in High Technology and Changes in War Form," Fang Liangqing, pp. 100-105.

Number 2, 2000
"On Military Foresight in the Information Age," Chen Xiaowei, pp. 154-157.

Number 1, 2000
There were no articles fitting the topics outlined above although one article discussed "modern war".

Numbers 5 and 6, 1999
No issues of these numbers were available for review.

Number 4, 1999
There were no articles fitting the topics. This issue contained four articles on Kosovo.

Number 3, 1999
"Analysis of Opposition in Operational Command in High-Tech Conditions," Zuo Quandian and Guo Ming, pp. 111-118.
This issue also contained four articles on Kosovo.

Number 2, 1999
"'Subduing the Enemy without Fighting' and 'Information War,'" Wang Baocun, pp. 60-63.
"New Changes in the Build-up and Use of US Military Strength in the Information Age," Chen Bojiang, pp. 142-148.
This issue also contained seven articles on Kosovo.

Number 1, 1999
"Further Study of Features and Laws of High-Tech Local War and Improving Guidance in Winning High-Tech Local War," Fu Quanyou, pp. 6-14.
"Aimed at Development, Strengthening Study of Information Warfare Theory and Construction of Digital Army and Digital Battlefields," Yuan Banggen, pp. 46-51.
"On Features and Laws of Local War under High-Tech Conditions," Dai Yifang, pp. 82-86.
"Course and Development of Information Operations," Cui Yonggui, pp. 87-89.
"Views on Early Warning in High-Tech Local War," Zhai Xiaomin, pp. 90-93.
"Digest of Three Essays: Views on Problems of Preparations of High-Tech Local War; Prompt Decision—An Important Principle of War Guidance in High-Tech Local War;

Views on Countering High-Tech Weaponry with Conventional Weaponry," Fu Jichen, Zhang Uywu, Wang Shuhua, and Xu Xiaobin, pp. 94-99.

APPENDIX TWO: TAIWAN REPORT COMMENTS ON CHINESE IW CAPABILITIES AND PLA PERCEPTIONS OF OPERATION IRAQI FREEDOM

The purpose of this appendix is to offer selected translations explaining Taiwan's view of Chinese IW so that the reader can compare Eastern (Taiwan's) and Western views (as presented in this book) of Chinese IW. It also includes Taiwanese commentary on how China viewed the 2003 war in Iraq. This article is reprinted as originally published by FBIS with their permission for use in a government publication.

Unclassified

Taiwan: DPP Report on China's Military Strength: 'Software' Development
CPP20040106000205 Taipei Tung-Sen Hsin-Wen Pao WWW-Text in Chinese 20 Dec 03
Reference:
CPP20031230000011

[Chapter Seven of DPP report on China's Military Strength: "By Setting Information Warfare as the Core for Military Construction, the PLA Has Achieved Quite a Lot in the Preparation for High-tech War and the Cultivation of Military Talents. The Potential Impact of the Military Reform of the PLA on the Regional Security Can not be Overlooked."]

[FBIS Translated Text]

Report on the PRC's Military Strength
7-0: The Software Aspect of the PRC's Military Development
Chapter 7 The Software Aspect of the PRC's Military Development

Prelude

In recent years, the PRC's military modernization has been the focus of strategists and military observers' attention. In the view of many scholars, the growth of the PRC's military strength has caused a potential threat to the security in the Asian-Pacific region. However, some scholars held a different view. In their opinion, the growth of the PRC's military strength is not sufficient to cause serious threat to East Asia's security.

However, despite these viewpoints, these conclusions were mostly drawn from the analysis and evaluation of the PLA's weapon system. Very few scholars have engaged in study on the software aspect of the PRC's military construction. As a matter of fact, the PLA has in recent years followed Jiang Zemin's overall demand for "politically qualified, militarily tough, excellent work style and forceful guarantee" to continuously strengthen development in terms of quality and quantity and obtained quite a degree of progress both in terms of standardization and modernization.

At the same time, the PLA also learned many new concepts and gained knowledge through the study of the Gulf War and on the basis of which actively engaged in the research and development of a new way to fight war in order to win "high-tech war." In order to keep up with the global military thought and meet the need of winning high-tech war, the PRC thus proposed a new reform of the military with "information warfare" as the core in order to increase the combat efficiency of troops and to respond to future battle ground environment. In terms of practice, to successfully achieve the goal, cultivation of talents and legalization of military play a very important role. The former can develop the function of weapons to its utmost by elevating military cadres' professional knowledge and capability and increasing the troops' combat efficiency; the latter guarantees the organization and composition of the PLA and the implementation of education training through the legalization development.

By means of the above-mentioned measures, along with the introduction of new type of carriers and weapons, the PLA will be substantially elevated in terms of both quality and quantity. Therefore, the discussion of the PLA's development can never overlook the development in the software aspect.

In this chapter, the PLA's achievements in the shakeup and re-organization for information warfare, cultivation of military talents, and the military's legalization development will be highlighted. This chapter will end with a preliminary evaluation of the PRC's national defense budget hike and the elevation of its military strength. In so doing, it hoped to explore the impact of the software aspect of the PLA's construction on its military strength in different aspects and to test and verify the discussion of previous chapters on the hardware aspect of the PLA's development and help us gain a comprehensive understanding of the PRC's military strength.

The Report of the PRC's Military Strength
Chapter 7-1
The Lesson of War in Iraq; the Development of Troops for Information Warfare
Chapter 7 The Software Aspect of the PRC's Military Development
Part I. The Development of Troops for Information Warfare

In recent years, the PRC has invested a huge amount of money and manpower in the modernization of the PLA. In addition to the research and development and introduction of various types of advanced carriers and weapons, the PRC also spent all it could on the development of the military in the software aspect. The most famous example is the active development of military revolution oriented toward information warfare. There are two reasons why the PRC wanted to strengthen the capability for information warfare. First, it recognized that future warfare will be the information warfare or high-tech warfare with information as the main substance. The other is the consideration that in the future conflicts might take place between the PRC and the United States. Under the condition that the PRC is inferior to the United States in terms of military strength, the only possibility for the PRC to win the war is by paralyzing the

US military computers and civilian computer systems. Based on this recognition, the PRC has aggressively reinforced the development related to information warfare in order to meet the demand of future warfare and asymmetrical warfare.

First, the Lesson of War in Iraq for the Development of PLA for Information Warfare

The biggest characteristic of the War in Iraq is the widespread use of non-contact battle in this war. Non-contact battle refers to a type of military operation in which opposing parties combined the systems of command, control, communication, intelligence, information, monitor, and surveillance as well as long-range precision weapons to launch attack outside the visual range of the enemy and the firing range of regular weapons. The US-British coalition mainly adopted two types of long-range attacks. First, they launched Tomahawk cruise missiles from bases 800 to 1000 kilometers away from the targets. Second, warplanes launched cruise missiles or precision guidance weapons from 40-50 kilometers away from the targets.

The US-British coalition has not encountered strong resistance from the Iraqi troops in this war. The main reason is that it adopted such non-contact type of operation as long range attack. According to the estimation by military experts, at least 60 percent of the Iraqi ground targets were destroyed by the US-British coalition through non-contact attack. Under the circumstances, the Iraqi troops were hit badly, and it could not effectively counter-attack the non-contact attack launched by the US-British coalition. Therefore, during the entire period of war, it could not gather enough troops to engage in decisive battle with the US and British ground forces.

Another characteristic of the war in Iraq is that the sensor-to-shooter integration of the US army has gained a ground-breaking elevation. For example, the US army used such non-human flight carriers as Global Hawk and Predator to shoot and transmit real-time or close to real-time battle ground images to guide fighting planes to attack the targets. The most famous of all is in the decapitation action when the US army learned about the actual location of Saddam Hussein through intelligence, it could in a very short period of time gather B-52 bombers to launch four 2000-pound bombs on the spot. This kind of high-degree integration between command, control, communication, intelligence, information, monitor and surveillance systems as well as weapon carriers and systems will become the focus of the military development for various countries in the future.

In addition, precision weapons such as Tomahawk cruise missiles and Joint Direct Attack Munitions (JADM) [preceding five words in English] were also widely used on the battle ground. It is estimated that its percentage in the total ammunition used is 80 percent. Compared to the 7.5 percent in the Gulf War, the 35 percent in the Kosovo War, and the 60 percent in the war in Afghanistan, the percentage is much higher.

Therefore, the war in Iraq will have certain important lesson for the development of informationization for the PRC. First, the military operation in the information age will no longer be the traditional contact battle of frontline contact; instead, it will be non-contact, non-linear, and long-range type of operation. Second, the digitalization of the battle ground is the most important military technology development in the information age. Through the combination of command, control, communication, intelligence, information, monitor, surveillance and long-range weapons, the goal of reducing command levels and shortening command time is achieved, which is highly conducive for the increase of combat efficiency. As in the Gulf War, the many measures in the war in Iraq, in addition to illustrating the importance of information war in modern warfare, also tested and verified the combined effect of the joint force of information, strength, and mobility. All these results are conducive to encouraging the PRC to continue to undertake the military revolution centering on information warfare.

Second, the PRC's Preparation for Information Warfare at Present

In May 1997, at a conference held by the Fourth Department [ECM and Radar] of the General Staff Headquarters of the PLA, military personnel proposed that the PLA establish the highest level "information warfare leading team" to direct theory, research and development work of information warfare for all armed forces. In the meantime, they called for the strengthening of the development of information warfare equipment, with particular attention to the overall integration of equipment, enlargement of the strength of reforming existing equipment by information technology and do a good work on the "information defense" system engineering. In October the same year, the PLA for the first time undertook a computer internet virus combat exercise. Two division command headquarters under a group army in the Shenyang military district launched attack on each other with computer viruses.

At the end of 1997, the PLA engaged in a military exercise of information warfare by real people. From the exercise of information network combat and computer virus attack and defense under simple communications environment to the comprehensive warfare such as soft kill and hard destruction in "united battle," the PRC has through many information combat exercises and computer simulation in various "military zones" engaged in the work of deepening, testing and verifying and become more and more sophisticated.

Therefore, we know that the PLA's information warfare has entered the stage of empirical testing. In addition, the PLA also included the military information network into the overall planning of the development of national information network to establish as soon as possible the network combat capability and adapt to the change of war type in order to contain and resist the invasion of network by hostile countries and to maintain the safety of important network and national security. Thus, information warfare is no longer an abstract concept for the PLA but has step by step been implemented in empirical testing and real battle field.

Third, the Development of C4ISR

Regardless of the approach the PRC will adopt to build the momentum for information warfare, without doubt, the organization and development of its information warfare capability will be centered on the integration of command, control, communication, intelligence, information, monitor, and surveillance, which will be further combined with its military strength and fire power in an effective way in order for sensors and weapons to become one. In this process, information technology will play an important role.

As a matter of fact, when the PRC pushed forward the "863 project," it had included the electronic and automatic control system related to C4ISR into the key items for research and development. Most important of all, information technology is the most representative military and civilian technology. In the future, the PRC can engage in the research, development, and integration of C4ISR equipment under the dual considerations of supporting national economic development and strengthening the combat capability of the PLA.

At present, the important aspects of the PRC's organization and development of C4ISR includes: employing large computers to build a central nervous system network and implement united simulation operation combat exercises; developing strategy data link, systematizing and standardizing military data transmission; establishing satellite receiving capability, and in cooperation with early warning measures establishing the three armed forces' three-dimensional command, control and combat capability; developing light-fiber communication network, increasing troops' automatized command system, and strengthening the capability to resist electro-magnetic interference.

Under the situation that the PRC might become the country with the most advanced telecommunications infrastructure, all this and the PRC's recent efforts in strengthening the construction of civilian telecommunications business enabled the PRC's command, control, communication, intelligence, information, monitor and surveillance capability to demonstrate cross-generation high-speed development along with the transfer of civilian technology and the spill-over effect of a high degree of telecommunicationization.

Fourth, Prospect and Challenge

Based on the consideration that the war in the future will be mainly based on information warfare, the PLA established under the second department of the General Staff Headquarters "the department of scientific equipment" to engage in various kinds of offense and defense plans for computer information warfare. In addition, the PRC also used unmanned carriers to serve as the platform for electronic warfare. It also deployed satellite communication jammers and even engaged in the research of the possibility of interrupting the United States' global positioning system, expanding the area of information attack to space and outer-space. In recent years, the PRC has made the following important achievements in information warfare development: (1) through commercial sale imported from the United States super-computer, decoding technology, and micro-processing machine technology; (2) paved along the costal line on the Southeast region 37000 kilometers of light-fiber communications network, built navigation towers and established a network along the coastline; (3) strengthened the momentum of the command, control, communication, and intelligence system of resisting

157

interruption, built firewalls on important software; (4) engaged in quantitative production and deployment of electro-magnetic pulse (EMP) [preceding three words in English] micro Sievert nuclear warheads; (5) introduced the equipment for research and development of electronic warfare and strengthened three armed forces' capabilities in engaging in electronic military operation.

Even though the PRC encountered many limitations in the development of information warfare, such as the lack of information talent, insufficient information infrastructure, and the low quality of military personnel, under the direction of "winning regional war under high technology condition," it will continue to develop the equipment and system related to information warfare.

It is noteworthy that as the PRC gradually became the world's largest supplier of information equipment and the momentum and techniques of its information industry is on the rise, in the future, with the assistance of "military-civilian dual-use" technology, the PRC's momentum for information warfare will double that in the past. In implementing either strategic or tactical action, it will definitely exert quite an impact on regional security and the stability in the Taiwan Strait.

Report of the PRC's Military Strength
7-2: Cultivation Project of High-Tech Military Talents
Chapter 7. The Software Aspect of the PRC's Military Development
Part II. Cultivation Project of High-Tech Military Talents

Under the situation that the pursuit of qualitative and quantitative advantage has become the trend for the military competition, modern warfare has become high-tech and three-dimensional warfare. How to elevate military cadres' professional and main duty knowledge and ability of is an important lesson for the military of various countries in their military development.

In recent years, the equipment of the PRC's three armed forces and strategic missile force has gradually been modernized. However, the concept, thinking, professional education, training method and the command, control procedure have not been effectively matched up. Therefore, the PRC has continued to strengthen the range and depth of cultivation of talents in recent years.

The PRC chairman Jiang Zemin pointed out, "talent is the basis of promoting the military, we must treat the cultivation and fostering of a large quantity of high quality talents as the basis of the military's modernization construction grand plan" and "cultivating military cadres by means of civilian higher education is in line with global military development trend." Based on this policy direction, "strengthening the military by means of technology and promoting the military by means of technology" has become the main theme for the PRC's military modernization development in the future. The importance of cultivation of high-tech talents is increasing day by day.

First, Adjustment of the PRC's High-Tech Military Talents Cultivation System

The main change of the PRC's military education began in the early 1980s. In 1981, the PRC implemented "academic degree system." In 1982, the PLA established "all-army academic degree leading team." In the meantime, the PLA granted master's degree to its first group of graduate students. The PLA established the educational system of cultivating and training its own graduate students pursuing for "master's" and "doctoral" degrees.

In June 1986, the PRC's Central Military Commission, in accordance with the decision of "the 13th military academies conference," promulgated "the decision concerning military academy education reform" and planned to engage in reform of military academy on the basis of existing command and professional technological school system. The command academy would be divided into the three levels of elementary, middle, and higher levels; professional technology institutes would be divided into middle and high levels. Until then, the PRC's command academy and professional institutes can be professionally divided, which would be conducive for cultivating professional and high-quality talents adaptive to modern technology warfare.

In addition, in order to elevate the quality of military officers, the PRC established National Defense University in 1985, in order for the middle and higher levels of military officers to engage in advanced education. Furthermore, in order to improve the problem of waste of resources and low efficacy, low quality of cadres and to meet the need of future warfare, the PLA in 1999 established 26 new military academies by means of integration and re-organization. In 1998, the General Staff Headquarters held learning classes targeting the presidents of military academies and proposed the slogan of "three high's," claiming to cultivate personnel with "three high" proficient skills from now on to the 21st century. The so-called "three high's" referred to "high" personal quality that can use "high" technological equipment in response to "high"- tech warfare.

In addition, the PLA also cooperated with well-known universities in various localities to cultivate talents with master's degree for the military and to facilitate the teaching and research needs of military academies. Furthermore, a reserve military officers corps was established in well-known universities to attract students to join the military and to establish "oriented student" system, allowing those students with lower scores for college entrance exams to enter famous universities to study and serve in the military after graduation. Through the above-mentioned related measures, the PLA has expanded the source of military officers and accelerated the elevation of military officers' quality. This is helpful for the PLA in achieving the goal of modernization.

Second, the Evaluation of Current PLA Leading Cadre Team's Quality

During the period of the "Tenth Five Year Plan," the PRC's military listed the elevation of the quality of officers and soldiers as the key point of military development. After many years' efforts, the quality of the PRC's leading cadres has been substantially elevated. For example, in 1988, over 58 percent of the high-ranking officers above the army level had received education at military schools or academies. Until 1994, 97 percent of the high-ranking military officers had received various kinds of advanced education; over 55 percent of the military officers had professional education. The percentage of new generation of military officers who had secondary education and advanced education is higher than the former. Based on the above-mentioned data, it is not difficult to see that the PLA has spent quite a lot of efforts in elevating the quality of cadres.

The indicators for evaluating the military's quality are plenty. The education level of high-ranking military officers is not sufficient to illustrate the quality of the overall leading cadre team. For example, the pro-PRC Hong Kong periodical, "Kuang Chiao Ching," indicated that at present the overall quality of the PLA officers remained low. Even if the degree of long-distance university, correspondence education, and part-time university were included, less than half of the PLA officers do not have university degree. Compared to other strong military countries, it is comparatively low.

Overall speaking, the quality of PLA's military officers and soldiers remained low, the majority of whom lacked the learning and cultivation of technology and mechanics. Although in recent years the PRC's military has adopted certain measures in a bold and resolute manner in order to improve the condition of low quality of the PLA's leading cadres, due to the fact that the cultivation of talents cannot be achieved in one step, the PRC's attempt to elevate the overall quality of cadres in a short period of time will face many challenges in the practical and structural aspects.

It is noteworthy that in recent years, the PRC's model of military modernization is to "skip a generation," [preceding three words in English] that is, directly entering the stage of research, development, and application of new generation weapons. This approach can make use of the "heterogeneity" and "asymmetry" in technology to rapidly elevate the combat capability and combat efficiency of troops. However, it also caused a great challenge for the cultivation and training of personnel. Because of the enormous number of the PLA troops, to demand the elevation of the overall quality of troops in a short period of time is like searching for fish on a tree.

Even though there remained many defects, undeniably, when the PRC's military institutions were more and more controlled by technocrats who have professional education training, the demand for professional talents will increase. What is to come next will be the continuation of cultivation of high-quality talents.

On the other hand, the cadres of the revolutionary generation have gradually demised and fazed out, and the new generation of military officers tended to accept modernized warfare concept. The interaction of the two factors is helpful for the PRC's military to develop toward the direction of professionalization, which has potential and positive impact on the PRC military's continuation of the cultivation of high-quality talents and on the elevation of cadres' quality at the leading level.

Third, the Effect of Knowledge Military on the Development of Military Talents

The transition from the labor intensive feature to technology intensive feature is an important change in modern warfare, which also is clearly reflected in the PRC's military development strategy of "two fundamental changes." The post-Cold War experiences of the Gulf War and Kosovo War showed that reform of military's internal system is an effective measure to guarantee innovation in the area of military. Under the trend of "knowledge economy" era, how to develop "learning organization" [preceding two words in English] is an important move to respond to the challenge in the future.

Likewise, for the military, in order to respond to the "uncertain" and "unpredictable" future, achieving "knowledge military" through "organization learning" is the only effective approach. However, an organization will not learn by itself. Those who can directly learn knowledge and apply it on work are the individuals in organization. Therefore, by striving for individuals who have learning and innovating abilities, creating learning environment favorable for them, and establishing mechanism and culture for mutual cooperation and sharing can the existing effect of "knowledge military" be developed.

In this regard, the PRC has encountered many challenges in the process of developing knowledge military, such as the needless duplicated military organizations that cannot adapt to the efficient and flexible management thinking of knowledge military.

In addition, the ideologically rigid bureaucratic organization operation and the lack of effective integration between parallel levels are the biggest obstacles for the PLA to engage in "knowledge military" management. In other words, if the PRC regarded "knowledge military" as the direction for future military construction, then it will try every possible means to eliminate existing set pattern, which will accelerate its demand for high-quality talents.

On the other hand, if batches and batches of high-quality talents continue to enter the military system, by means of the process of transition from "quantitative change to qualitative change," the PLA's internal cultural and operation procedure can be gradually changed and military organization that is in line with modernization development can be established. In this regard, knowledge military plays a role of facilitator for the cultivation of military talents. Most importantly, the implementation effect of the latter is also related to whether the goal of the former can be achieved.

For example, knowledge military stresses the importance of united military operation. In order to elevate the cadres' accomplishments in united military operation, Nanjing Army Command Academy signed with the air force, the navy, and the strategic missile force respectively "cooperation agreement" and established 20 different trans-army educational and scientific research and testing bases. By means of the interaction between different military branches, the officers under training were led by the personnel on the bases to participate in exercises and jointly study and explore the regularity and method of joint operation and learn to control the characteristics of command in different military branches. By so doing, the students gained profound understanding of the basic characteristics of command in operation of various kinds of military branches. More importantly, the students' consciousness of united operation has been strengthened and the quality and quantity of cultivation of joint operation force heightened.

From the above example, it is not difficult to see that knowledge military has quite a far-reaching impact on the cultivation of high-quality military talents as well as certain function of guidance. Therefore, after the PRC further recognized the importance of knowledge military, it will definitely speed up the cultivation of high-quality military talents.

Report on the PRC's Military Strength
7-4 Firepower Intensive and Brain Intensive Rather than Labor Intensive
Chapter 7 The Software Aspect of the PRC's Military Development
Part Four. the PRC's National Defense Budget

Since 1989, the PRC's annual national defense budget has continued to grow by double digits, causing concerns by the outside world over the PRC's military expansion. On the contrary, some people have different viewpoints. To them, the growth of the PRC's national defense budget has been set off by the inflation as a result of the economic growth or been used for the improvement of the pay for the PLA. Therefore, the budget hike is not related to the PRC's military expansion. However, these two viewpoints have their shortcomings. The fundamental reason is that the PRC's national defense budget is only a part of its military expense. To estimate the PRC's military development simply by its national defense budget will reach partial conclusion.

Therefore, while discussing this question, the motive of the PRC's national defense budget hike and the relationship between national defense budget and military strength increase must be analyzed in order to help us understand the development of the PRC's military strength in the future.

First, Analysis of the Factors of National Defense Increase after the End of the Cold War

After the end of the Cold War when various countries enjoyed "profits of peace," they also reduced national defense budget one after another and downsized troops and transferred the large quantity of resources that were invested in national defense department to economy and trade in the hope to strengthen economic competitiveness and elevate the overall strength of the country. Contrary to the mainstream development pattern in the world, the PRC after the end of the Cold War has increased rather than reduced its national defense budget. Compared to the 1980s, its national defense budget has increased in a large scale. The factors involved included national economic development, military strategic adjustment and the structural change of military power.

National Economic Development

In the early period of the PRC's promotion of "four modernizations," Deng Xiaoping proposed the guidelines of "economy as the center of construction," "military development must obey the grand plan of economic construction," and "the troops must live under tight belt." With the upturn of the PRC's national economic development and the success of reform and opening up policy, correspondingly the PRC's national defense budget can maintain a high degree of growth everyday.

It is not difficult to see from table one that the amount of annual increase of the PRC's national defense budget is positively correlated with the change of gross national product (GNP). In other words, as the GNP increased, the PRC's national defense budget also increased. At present, the PRC's national defense budget takes up about 1.5 percent of the GNP. Compared to the 3 to 4 percent in major Western countries, such as the United Kingdom, the United States, France, and Germany, there is still quite a room for growth (not included those budget hidden in other departments). If the PRC can maintain the annual economic growth rate of 7 to 8 percent, in 20 years, it will become the second largest economy in the world, next to the United States. Under the circumstances, the PRC can invest considerable resources into national defense and help speed up the completion of military modernization.

Military Strategic Adjustment

In recent years, the PRC's military strategy has been to change from winning a regular war under ordinary conditions to winning a regional war under modern high-technology under the guidance of "positive defense." Based on this consideration, the PRC set the direction of military operation toward the Southeast coastal region, South China Sea, and Sino-Indian borders. In order to strive for military edge, the PRC has invested a large amount of resources to engage in military modernization.

In order to win the regional war under high-technology condition and effectively project its influence to China's neighboring areas, the PRC has in recent years continued to introduce various kinds of advanced carriers that can project its military power, including SU-27, SU-30 fighter, Kilo submarines, and Modern Destroyers. These carriers are not manufactured by the PRC, and the introduction of these carriers will definitely cost a large amount of foreign exchange. Even though it was reported that the PRC once used the method of "bartering" to engage in weapon procurement, yet the percentage of which in the total amount is still very low. Since the PRC's military technology still lagged behind the Western advanced countries, in the future it still has to rely on imported weapons and carriers to speed up the pace of the modernization of PLA. Under the circumstances, the PRC's national defense budget will increase, yet the increase of military strength can be immediately achieved.

The Change of the Structure of Military Force

In addition to the preparation for military struggle, the PRC's military has also made a certain degree of adjustment in military development. When the military development made the transition from "quantitative scale" to "qualitative effect" or from the "labor intensive" feature to "technology intensive" feature, it must engage in research, development, and procurement of advanced weapons and carriers and invest more national defense resources as a response. In other words, the upgrade of the structure of military power meant that the investment in national defense will become more and more capital- and scale-oriented.

Modern warfare is high-technology warfare in which it is "firepower intensive" and "brain intensive" rather than "labor intensive." Therefore, the guerilla war fought with "millet and rifles" is not in line with high-tech war under modern condition. Modern war needs sophisticated weapons and high quality talents, and the procurement of the former and the cultivation of the latter both need the investment of a huge amount of capital.

In the future, the PRC will reduce 200,000 soldiers. However, the reduction of military force does not mean that the national defense budget will be reduced correspondingly. If its military development in the future marches toward the direction of high technology, the cost for every unit of investment will likely to increase in a large scale. At present, the PRC's policy of "technology promoting training and technology strengthening the military force" has not changed. For the establishment of a "high effective and combined" modern military force, the PRC's military investment will definitely continue to increase.

Second, Analysis of the Use of the PRC's National Defense Budget and Elevation of Military Strength

To the annual increase of national defense budget in recent years, the PRC's official defense is that the increase was used to improve the living standard of the soldiers, to create a sound protection system for the soldiers, to maintain the normal operation of the military, and to elevate the PRC's own national defense needs. In terms of the amount of the PRC's national defense budget, if the above-mentioned various kinds of expenses were deducted, it cannot maintain the enormous structure of military force of the PLA.

In addition to the enormous number of soldiers, the PRC's military not only is equipped with various kinds of traditional weapons, it also has a strategic nuclear weapon troops that ranks third in the world in terms of scale. In November 1995, the PRC for the first time publicized its national defense policy whitepaper. The whitepaper pointed out, "China's national defense development is low investment type" and "from now one, as long as the national security is not facing obvious threats, it is impossible for national defense budget to show a large scale of increase."

With regard to the two statements, there is quite a large gap between what is true and what is claimed. In other words, the PRC definitely has a method that is different from other countries to maintain the enormous number of PLA troops under the limited national defense budget.

As is widely known, the PRC's national defense budget as was publicized was very different from the actual national defense expenses. As estimated by the Western countries, the difference ranged from two to three times. This is because the PRC's military hid much of its budget under other departments. For example, the budget for weapon production is directly appropriated by the State Council to related companies under the national defense industry department. The budget for armed police mainly came from the budget for public security department.

In addition, central and local governments will be responsible for the budget for national defense technology and for militia and reserve service troops. Therefore, the PRC's actual national defense expense far exceeded the number publicized. Furthermore, there are many related budgets that were not directly listed in the national finance, such as the income from the PLA's commercial activities in the past and the enormous amount of foreign exchange obtained by the PRC's arms sale to other countries.

In recent years, the PRC introduced from Russia a large amount of advanced carriers and weapons, such as Su-27 and Su-30 fighters, S300 air defense missiles, Kilo submarines and Modern Destroyers. This equipment is expensive to obtain. Military observers all regarded it as the main reason for the sudden hike in the PRC's national defense budget in recent years. However, Japanese expert, Hiramatsu Shigeo, who has for a long time studied the PRC's military held a different viewpoint. According to his speculation, the expenses for the PRC's procurement of various kinds of weapons were mostly not listed in its national defense budget.

Hiramatsu Shigeo pointed out that the reason for the PRC's national defense budget hike in 1994 was the increase of the expense for personnel. The continued growth since 1994 has been the result of constantly holding large-scale military exercises for the sake of checking the achievements for the "military training reform" implemented since 1993. Under the situation that the PRC's national defense budget is implicit in various departments, it is very difficult for us to make a judgment regarding the relationship between its national defense budget and the elevation of its military strength.

However, if economic growth is used as the basis for consideration, the PRC's national defense budget still has a room for increase. More specifically speaking, when apparent threat becomes present in the PRC's neighboring security environment, it has sufficient economic ability to bear the additional military expenses.

A Brief Summary

In the past ten years, issues related to the development of the PRC's military strength have gradually drawn attention from scholars of international relations and strategists. However, most of the issues for discussion centered on the hardware aspect of the PLA's development.   The analysis of related software of the development also mainly focused on the reconstruction of organization.   However, the software or qualitative aspect of the development is never simply the downsizing of military personnel, reorganization of military power, and the effective use of military expenses.

As a matter of fact, the software aspect of the development covered a wide variety of aspects, such as military thoughts, cultivation of talents, and the development of a legal system.   The above-mentioned issues have for a long time not received attention, and scholars in this area are also far and few between.   For example, legal construction will affect the progress of the military's normalization or lead the military to be under the control of   the state and at least will cause impact on the existing party-military relationship.   Therefore, while discussing the future development of the PLA, the above-mentioned factors can never be overlooked.   Otherwise, it will be difficult to outline the direction for the future development of the PLA.

It is not difficult to discover from the above-mentioned analysis that the PLA has in the past ten years not only obtained groundbreaking achievements in the development of military hardware, but its achievements in software development do not let the former monopolize the limelight.   However, different from the hardware development, the software development needs many years before the effect can be present, and its achievements in a large degree are affected by the human factor.

Therefore, the policy must be consistent, and the implementation by the units at both high and low levels must be down-to-earth.   Otherwise, the software development is highly likely to be interrupted or disrupted and abandoned.   At present, the PLA's decision making is interfered by many political forces.   The phenomenon of "party leading the military" has subsided a bit but not entirely disappeared, which would cause certain negative influence on its undertaking of software development.

It is noteworthy that as the PRC's military paid more and more attention to the software aspect of development and continued to engage in research and development and introduction of advanced equipment, if it can effectively integrate the two, in the next ten years, the PLA will double its military strength and become a military force that can exert salient influence in the Asian-Pacific region.   If so, it will cause serious impact on the security in the region and Taiwan's stability.

Unclassified

GPO ☆ U.S. GOVERNMENT PRINTING OFFICE: 2005—769-68!